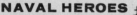

INDIANS

POCAHONTAS, *Seymour*
SACAGAWEA, *Seymour*
SEQUOYAH, *Snow*
SITTING BULL, *Stevenson*
SQUANTO, *Stevenson*
TECUMSEH, *Stevenson*

SOCIAL and CIVIC LEADERS

...ON,
...on
..., *Mason*
...ADDAMS, *Wagoner*
J. STERLING MORTON, *Moore*
JULIA WARD HOWE, *Wagoner*
JULIETTE LOW, *Higgins*
LILIUOKALANI, *Newman*
LUCRETIA MOTT, *Burnett*
MOLLY PITCHER, *Stevenson*
OLIVER WENDELL HOLMES, JR., *Dunham*
SUSAN ANTHONY, *Monsell*

NAVAL HEROES

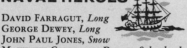

DAVID FARRAGUT, *Long*
GEORGE DEWEY, *Long*
JOHN PAUL JONES, *Snow*
MATTHEW CALBRAITH PERRY, *Scharbach*
OLIVER HAZARD PERRY, *Long*
RAPHAEL SEMMES, *Snow*
STEPHEN DECATUR, *Smith*

NOTED WIVES and MOTHERS

ABIGAIL ADAMS, *Wagoner*
DOLLY MADISON, *Monsell*
JESSIE FREMONT, *Wagoner*
MARTHA WASHINGTON, *Wagoner*
MARY TODD LINCOLN, *Wilkie*
NANCY HANKS, *Stevenson*
RACHEL JACKSON, *Govan*

SOLDIERS

ANTHONY WAYNE, *Stevenson*
BEDFORD FORREST, *Parks*
DAN MORGAN, *Bryant*
ETHAN ALLEN, *Winders*
FRANCIS MARION, *Steele*
ISRAEL PUTNAM, *Stevenson*
JEB STUART, *Winders*
NATHANAEL GREENE, *Peckham*
ROBERT E. LEE, *Monsell*
SAM HOUSTON, *Stevenson*
TOM JACKSON, *Monsell*
U. S. GRANT, *Stevenson*
WILLIAM HENRY HARRISON, *Peckham*
ZACK TAYLOR, *Wilkie*

SCIENTISTS and INVENTORS

ALBERT EINSTEIN, *Hammontree*
ALECK BELL, *Widdemer*
CYRUS MCCORMICK, *Dobler*
ELI WHITNEY, *Snow*
ELIAS HOWE, *Corcoran*
ELIZABETH BLACKWELL, *Henry*
GEORGE CARVER, *Stevenson*
GEORGE EASTMAN, *Henry*
HENRY FORD, *Aird and Ruddiman*
JOHN AUDUBON, *Mason*
LUTHER BURBANK, *Burt*
MARIA MITCHELL, *Melin*
ROBERT FULTON, *Henry*
SAMUEL MORSE, *Snow*
TOM EDISON, *Guthridge*
WALTER REED, *Higgins*
WILBUR AND ORVILLE WRIGHT, *Stevenson*
WILL AND CHARLIE MAYO, *Hammontree*

STATESMEN

ABE LINCOLN, *Stevenson*
ANDY JACKSON, *Stevenson*
DAN WEBSTER, *Smith*
FRANKLIN ROOSEVELT, *Weil*
HENRY CLAY, *Monsell*
JAMES MONROE, *Widdemer*
JEFF DAVIS, *de Grummond and Delaune*
JOHN MARSHALL, *Monsell*
TEDDY ROOSEVELT, *Parks*
WOODROW WILSON, *Monsell*

Stephen Foster

Boy Minstrel

Illustrated by Al Fiorentino

Stephen Foster

Boy Minstrel

By Helen Boyd Higgins

THE **BOBBS-MERRILL** COMPANY, INC.
A SUBSIDIARY OF HOWARD W. SAMS & CO., INC.
Publishers • INDIANAPOLIS • NEW YORK

To Josiah Kirby Lilly
Whose love of beauty in simple melodies
has kept alive the songs of
Stephen Foster

Illustrations

Numerous smaller illustrations

Contents

Books by Helen Boyd Higgins

ALEC HAMILTON: THE LITTLE LION
JULIETTE LOW: GIRL SCOUT
NOAH WEBSTER: BOY OF WORDS
STEPHEN FOSTER: BOY MINSTREL
WALTER REED: BOY WHO WANTED TO KNOW

★ Stephen

Foster

Boy Minstrel

A Very
Special Day

STEVIE FOSTER was ready first. He ran in and out of the house, shouting to his older brothers.

"Hurry up, Mit!" he called. "The boat will go off and leave us."

The day was the Fourth of July—the Fourth of July in the faraway year 1830.

The four younger Foster boys were going on a river picnic. Their names were Henry, Dunning, Morrison, and Stephen. Mit was Morrison's nickname. He was seven.

This was the first time that Stevie had gone on a picnic without his mother, and he was excited. "Hurry up, Dunning! Hurry up, Henry!"

11

he called again. "We won't get there in time if we don't hurry."

Mother Foster smiled. She patted the boys on the shoulders as they ran past her down the steps.

"Remember, boys," she called. "Stevie isn't as old as the rest of you. Take good care of him." Henry was fourteen and Dunning was nine. They were used to looking after the others.

"I'm four years old today," said Stevie. "I can take care of myself."

"He'll be all right, Ma," shouted Henry. "It's his birthday. He should do something different."

As the boys ran down the road the kitchen door banged and Tray, the family's black and white dog, trotted after the boys.

The door banged again. This time a young colored girl came racing around the corner of the house. She stopped by Mrs. Foster's side. She was the little maid who helped Mrs. Foster in the kitchen.

"I declare, Miss Liza," she said. "I just put that Tray dog in my closet so's he couldn't go with the boys. Now look at him."

"You'll have to go get him, Lieve," said Mother Foster. "It would never do for him to go on the picnic."

Lieve ran after him and soon brought him back. Then she and Mrs. Foster stood watching the boys as they hurried through the gate.

"Our boys are sure handsome, Miss Liza," said Lieve. "I hope Stevie ain't going to get tuckered out. He's mighty cute and growing like a jimson weed, but he ain't big like the others."

"The boys will take care of him," said Mother Foster. "Don't worry."

Just then there was a scattering of stones on the drive and Mr. William Barclay Foster drove up in his horse and buggy. He was on his way into town.

"I will bring William home with me this afternoon," he said to his wife. "The 'Napoleon' docks at four."

William Junior was the eldest son of the family. He was in business in another town, where he lived. Although he was still young, he was already making money.

"Maybe you'd better give Stevie a ride to the pike," said Mother Foster. "He's gone on the picnic with the other boys."

"He'll be fine," Mr. Foster said, smiling. "Eliza, my dear, you baby that boy too much."

Mr. Foster was a kindly man and a leader in his community. He sat very straight as he drove down the hill to the main road.

He owned a company that operated flatboats on the Ohio and Mississippi Rivers between Pittsburgh and New Orleans. Furs, flour, and other produce from the neighborhood of Pittsburgh were shipped south to be traded for sugar, coffee, and other merchandise brought to New Orleans

14

from the West Indies. In addition, he owned one hundred and twenty-one acres of rich Pennsylvania land which lay close to the Allegheny River, two miles from the fast-growing town of Pittsburgh.

As he turned into the main road leading to Pittsburgh, Mr. Foster waved to his wife. She waved in return, then went back in the house. It was a comfortable place known to all their friends as the White Cottage.

"Where are Miss Ann Eliza and Miss Etty, Lieve?" asked Mother Foster.

"They're makin' up the beds and tidyin' up the parlor," answered Lieve.

Mother Foster smiled. She was a tall, slender woman with an oval face and smooth dark hair. Her eyes were large and brown. Her hands were slim and soft.

Her little son Stevie—Stephen Collins Foster —looked very like his mother.

"Ann Eliza! Etty!" called Mother Foster.

"Here we are, Ma," called Etty. "I'm all finished now. May I go with the boys?"

"No, dear," said Ma. "You're almost a young lady, Henrietta. It isn't seemly for you to race about with the boys."

Henrietta—Etty for short—was nearly twelve. She was quick and laughing and had lots of fun. Always before now she had gone with the boys on their picnics.

"Ma," said Ann Eliza, "shall I help Lieve with the birthday cake?"

Ann Eliza was very different from Etty. She liked to help Mother in the kitchen and about the house. She was eighteen years old and had a great many beaus.

"That would be nice, dear. Be sure there are lots of nuts inside the cake."

"But Stevie is too little for nuts," said Ann Eliza. "You always said so."

Mother laughed. "Now Ann Eliza, there will be plenty for your young man, too."

Ann Eliza pouted and walked to the open door. "Here comes Dunning back," she said. "I wonder what he forgot."

"I forgot my lunch," shouted Dunning. "Where is it, Lieve?"

"Here it is," said Lieve. "How's my Stevie?"

"Oh, he's all right. Henry is riding him on his shoulders," said Dunning. "Pa stopped and wanted to take him part of the way, but Stevie didn't want to go."

Etty looked again at her mother. "Couldn't I, please?" she asked.

"Henrietta, you know you mustn't beg, dear."

Dunning raced off down the road.

"Hold on to Tray," shouted Mit from down the road. "Stevie was trying to get him to go with us. But Mr. Merrill said no dogs could come, so you'll have to keep Tray there."

Mr. Merrill was the minister. He was taking the boys and girls on the trip. Tray whined and tried to get away.

"I know just how you feel, Tray," said Etty. "Come on, I'll race you to the orchard."

Mrs. Foster watched them race away. Then she and Ann Eliza and Lieve went into the White Cottage to get ready for the birthday supper for Stevie.

When Dunning reached the other boys, they were all marching in time to their own singing. Henry led, with Stevie on his shoulders.

"Boom—boom—boom, boom, boom," Stevie shouted as he waved a stick above his head.

"Here we go marching. Here we go marching," sang the boys.

Neighborhood children, boys and girls, were joining the Fosters. They all hurried down to the shore of the Allegheny River and trooped onto a flat-bottomed barge called the "Amanda K."

18

Red-faced Captain Peters was the skipper. Minister Merrill was the leader. He met each child as he came aboard.

The little boat that was to push the barge came puffing alongside.

"Is everyone aboard?" shouted Captain Peters.

"All accounted for," said Mr. Merrill.

"Then anchors aweigh! Everybody settle down till we get out a way."

Chairs and boxes were placed about the deck. Someone began to sing. Soon everyone joined.

"Father and I went down to camp,
    Along with Captain Goodwin;
    And there we saw the men and boys
    As thick as hasty puddin'.

"Yankee doodle, keep it up,
    Yankee doodle, dandy.
    Mind the music and the step
    And with the girls be handy."

They sang all the verses. Then someone started another favorite. They sang "Hail, Columbia" and "Swing Low, Sweet Chariot" and many other songs. Stevie sat on a pile of rope and kept time with all of them.

The time passed very quickly. There was so much to see. The barge passed the "Golden Belle," the most beautiful of all the river boats that traveled between Pittsburgh and Cincinnati.

About noon the "Amanda K" was pushed close to shore. It was now in an inlet of the great Ohio River.

Everyone grabbed his belongings. Mr. Merrill sprang across to land. The crowd followed. The boys started up the hill.

"Boys!" the minister called. "It's the Fourth of July, the birthday of our country. What shall we sing?"

"That new song about the flag," shouted someone. "What's the title?"

" 'The Spangled Banner,' " said another.

" 'The *Star*-Spangled Banner,' " said Mr. Merrill. "That's a fine song. Stevie Foster, come here a minute."

Stevie ran across the bank.

"It's your birthday, too, isn't it?"

"Yes, sir," said Stevie.

"Would you like to hold the flag while we sing?" said the minister.

Stevie's eyes sparkled. Mr. Merrill handed him a flag. Stevie stood very straight because he was so proud.

The sun shone on the twenty-four white stars on the blue ground of the flag. It made the red and white stripes gleam.

"Ready, everyone," said Mr. Merrill. "Sing!"

"Oh, say, can you see, by the dawn's early light," they all began.

Stevie felt little waves of excitement run up and down his neck. He stood as tall as he could.

The boys and girls sang all the verses.

Stevie's black hair blew across his eyes. His face was so hot that it was wet. He sang with the rest of the children.

"And the star-spangled banner in triumph
    shall wave
O'er the land of the free and the home of
    the brave."

Then Stevie began to wave the flag.

Mr. Merrill called, "Dinner on the bluff."

Everyone but Stevie raced up the path which

led to the bluff above the river. Even at a picnic Stevie was "making believe."

"I'm a soldier marching," he said to himself.

He walked very straight carrying the flagpole on his shoulder.

For a short time everyone was too busy eating to talk. Mr. Merrill broke the silence. He pointed to a steep, rocky hill a short distance away. "Did you all know that George Washington probably climbed that very hill in 1754?"

"Why?" asked Mit Foster.

"He and forty men were looking for a good location for a fort," Mr. Merrill said. "From the top of that hill he noticed that he could see far up the Allegheny and Monongahela Rivers, which meet there. He also noticed that he could see far down the Ohio River, which the Allegheny and Monongahela form. He decided that was a perfect place to build a fort."

"It's a sure thing no enemy could sneak up on

it," a boy said. "Is that pile of rocks part of the fort Washington built?"

"No, they're the ruins of the one which took the place of the fort he built," said Mr. Merrill.

"Let's play George Washington and have battles with—who was the enemy, Mr. Merrill?"

"The French and Indians."

"I'll be Washington," said Ben Colby.

"No, I will," said Dunning.

"Better draw stones," said Mr. Merrill.

Dunning ran down to the shore and brought back a handful of stones.

"The blue stone stands for Washington," he said. "Whoever picks it can be Washington."

The boys each picked a stone. Ben Colby picked the blue one.

Then the boys took sides. Some were Washington's men. Some were French, and others were Indians. Stevie stepped over to be with Washington's men.

"You can't play, Stevie," said Henry. "You couldn't keep up."

"But you said I could," said Stevie. "You said I——"

"Oh, let him tag along," said Ben, who could give orders because he was George Washington. "He won't bother us."

Stevie started over the rocks after the others. His legs were so short that he could not keep up with them. Several times the older boys stopped long enough to give him a boost. But he was soon left behind.

He began to look about for something to do. Just off the shore was a rowboat. Someone in the boat was singing. The voice sounded like Lieve's only it was deeper.

> "Swing low, sweet chariot,
> Comin' for to carry me home,"

came the song from the boat.

This was one of Lieve's favorite songs. She

sang it when she made bread. She sang it when Stevie was in the kitchen helping, because she knew that Stevie liked it, too.

Stevie walked down the shore. "Hello," he called. "Can I come out? Are you fishing?"

The song stopped. A man's head appeared.

"Sure, I'm fishin', little boy," he said. "I'm fishin' for my dinner."

"May I come out?" asked Stevie.

"Will you be mighty quiet and not scare the fish away?" said the old colored man.

"Of course," said Stevie.

The fisherman beckoned to him. Stevie sat down, took off his shoes and stockings and turned up his long trousers. Even in July the water was cold. Stevie waded slowly out to the boat. The fisherman helped him over the side.

"There you are, honey," said the old man.

"What's your name?" asked Stevie.

"Ned."

"Mine is Stevie Foster," said Stevie.

"Now you take hold of the line, Mister Stevie, and Ned'll take a little rest."

Stevie smiled. He took hold of the long fishing pole. A worm wriggled at the end of the line.

"Drop it in the water," said the old man. "That's it. Now, when old man fish bite, you just call Ned quick."

"I will," said Stevie. "Couldn't you sing a little more before you go to sleep? I like singing."

"Who said Ned's goin' to sleep? Just goin' to rest," said the old man.

Stevie watched the old man as he lay on the bottom of the boat. He was almost bald and the little hair he had left was white. He was very tall and his clothes were torn.

Soon he put his long black fingers to his mouth and began to hum.

As he blew through his fingers, it sounded a little as it did when Papa played the violin.

Suddenly the fishing pole and line dipped.

"Ned! Ned!" shouted Stevie.

Ned was up in a minute. "You sure got something, honey," he said. "Just you hold on. Ned is goin' to get him."

Stevie pulled. "It's an awful big fish," he shouted. "I can tell."

Stevie gave the line a jerk. At the end flopped a small but very lively fish. "I got it! I got it!" he shouted happily.

Ned smiled. He took the fish in his big hands and gave it a quick slap against the side of the boat. Then he took another worm from a tin can and put it on the hook.

"Must be another where that one came from," he said. "You get him, Mister Stevie. Then Ned'll clean him and cook him for supper."

Stevie stayed with Ned a long time. They talked about boats, and Ned tried to show Stevie how to sing through his fingers.

When they had four fish in the bottom of the boat, Ned climbed out and disappeared around the point of the cove.

"Where are you going?" called Stevie.

"You'll see," came the sound of Ned's voice.

The boat was anchored, safely, so Stevie went on fishing.

After a little while the old man came back. He had several hollow reeds in his hand. "Ned's goin' to fix a tuner for you," he said.

"A tuner? What's that?"

"A tuner. You know, honey, a little whistle so young Mister Stevie can play a song. You're goin' to play a mighty pretty song, too. You'll see."

As the old man whittled with his knife, Stevie sat close by his side. He saw Ned cut a nick from the top. Then he added four round holes down the side of the reed.

When this was finished, he put the reed to his

lips. He blew gently and a soft little sound came from the tuner.

"Let me. Let me," said Stevie.

"Blow easy," Ned warned.

Steve tried.

At first the sound was just a squeak. Then it became a tone. Stevie moved his fingers as he had seen the old man move his.

"There!" said Ned. "What did Ned tell you? There's a nice song."

Stevie was delighted. His fingers flew. The notes became clearer.

"Stevie, Stevie!" shouted someone from shore. "Where are you?"

"It's Henry," said Stevie. "I have to go."

"Here he is," shouted Ned. "I'm bringin' him." He picked Stevie up and carried him across the water to dry land.

"Thank you, Ned," said Stevie. "Thank you for my tuner."

30

"Thank you, Mister Stevie," said Ned. "Ned's going to like those fishes fine." He smiled and waved at Stevie as Stevie followed the other boys out of sight.

"Did Washington take the fort?" Stevie asked Henry.

"Of course. Why did you run away?"

"I didn't run away. You did. I just fished with Ned and he made me a tuner. Listen."

When they reached the home wharf, their older brother William met the boys with the carriage. They were very glad not to have to walk home. Their feet were tired and they were cross —all but Stevie. He was excited and happy. He wasn't in the least tired because he had been sitting in the boat all afternoon.

When they were all tidied up, Mother Foster called them to supper. "Stevie may sit up here at the head of the table because it's his birthday," she said.

Stevie ate and ate and ate. He was so full when Lieve brought in his birthday cake that he could hardly cut the first piece.

It was a beautiful cake. The nuts stuck out even through the icing. There were four pine cones on the top. In the very middle was a small red apple.

"That's to grow big on, Stevie," said Ann Eliza.

It was still light when the Fosters were finished and went out of doors.

"Stevie shall choose the story tonight," said Pa. "What shall it be, my son?"

There was an old Darkey, his name was Un - cle Ned,

Stevie Chooses a Story

WHENEVER the Fosters were together after supper, their father told them a story. He knew a great many exciting stories because he had traveled so much. He knew Indian stories. He knew stories about accidents on the river boats. Once he had been almost captured by pirates. That was the story Dunning and Mit liked best.

"Come now," said Pa. "Put on your thinking cap, Stevie."

Stevie settled close to Pa. Mit sat on the step by his side. The rest of the family were sitting here and there on the porch. Ma and Ann Eliza sat on chairs.

"Stevie carried the American flag today," said Mit proudly.

"He did!" said Pa. "Did you sing 'Hail, Columbia' when he held it?"

"No," said Stevie, "we sang a new song. It's about stars and spangles and fighting."

"That's 'The Star-Spangled Banner,'" Pa said. "There was a bloody battle going on when that song was written."

"Is it a story?" asked Stevie.

"One of the best," said Pa.

"Then I'll choose it, Pa."

"Someday I'm sure everyone in our country will know the story about that song," Pa said.

"Is it a 'Once upon a time' story?" asked Mit.

"No, not really, because it was written only sixteen years ago, in 1814, the year I bought this farm," Mr. Foster said. Stevie pushed closer to his father's side.

"Be quiet, Mit, and you, too, Stevie," said

Dunning. "You mean during the War of 1812, don't you, Pa?"

"What war was that?" asked Mit.

"Our second war with Great Britain."

"Were you a soldier in it, Pa?" asked Mit.

"Your father was very much in it," Mother Foster said quickly. "Pa, the little boys should know what you did for your country during those trying times."

"I'll tell them," William said with pride.

"Pa was the Deputy Commissioner of Purchases for our army in this district and——"

"That means that Pa was head of the committee that bought supplies for our army in this neighborhood," Henry explained. "But when the army needed food and clothes and ammunition there wasn't any money to buy them."

"So Pa paid for them himself and even borrowed money to finish the job——"

"It will be paid back," Mr. Foster said.

"But when did Mr. Key write the song?" Stevie asked. "What about that, Pa?"

"After the British had burned down our White House in Washington, they sailed north to take the wealthy city of Baltimore," William went on. "But when the British fleet attacked Fort McHenry near the city they were beaten. Mr. Key wrote 'The Star-Spangled Banner' that night during the battle."

"Then Pa helped win that battle with the supplies he bought, didn't he?" said Mit, jumping to his feet.

"No, no, boys," said Pa quickly. "By that time the soldiers whom I had equipped had already marched south to defend New Orleans. The rest of their supplies were taken secretly down the Ohio and Mississippi Rivers by boat. They arrived at New Orleans just three days before the big battle."

"Then you helped win that battle, didn't you,

Pa?" Mit said. "Our soldiers couldn't have fought so well if they hadn't had your supplies."

"That's right, and it was a very important battle, too," Henry said.

"I feel proud all over, Pa," Mit said.

"I do, too," said Stevie. "I feel just as I did when I held the flag. I'm ready for the story now, Pa."

"Yes, go on, Pa," Dunning said. "Begin at the beginning, with Dr. Beanes."

"Well, in August, 1814, the feeling against the English was very strong all over the country. It was so strong that Dr. Beanes, who lived in the town of Upper Marlborough, near Washington, D.C., locked up three British soldiers without any reason except that he was angry."

"I'd have locked them up, too," said Mit.

"I would, too," said Stevie. "What happened next, Pa?"

"This action of Dr. Beanes was quite unfair,"

38

said Pa. "The British heard of it and captured Dr. Beanes and took him out on one of their war ships anchored in the bay.

"Now, Dr. Beanes had two very good friends, Francis Scott Key and John Skinner. These two young men went to President Madison and asked his permission to go out to the ship and try to get the British to release Dr. Beanes.

"The President of the United States gave his consent. The two young men went in a small boat out to the enemy ship.

" 'Who comes there?' shouted the sailor on watch on the ship.

" 'Messengers from President Madison,' said Mr. Key.

" 'Come aboard and show your papers,' said the guard.

"A rope ladder was let down over the side of the ship. The two Americans climbed up onto the deck. Mr. Key gave the message from President Madison to the sentinel. Then Francis Scott Key and John Skinner waited."

"Weren't they afraid?" asked Mit.

"If they had been afraid they wouldn't have gone," said Dunning. "Go on, Pa."

"By and by the sailor returned. He led the two Americans into the cabin of Admiral Cockburn, the commander of the British fleet.

"He listened carefully to what they had to say. Then he frowned and fingered some papers on his table.

"Francis Key and John Skinner felt the chills go up and down their backs. Here they were out in the middle of Chesapeake Bay on an enemy ship and the Commander was frowning.

"He pushed back his chair and walked up and down the floor. Suddenly he turned about.

" 'I will grant your request, young man,' he said to Mr. Key. 'But you are not to return to shore for a few hours longer.'

40

"Then the Commander sent for Dr. Beanes.

" 'I would like to have your promise, gentlemen,' he said, 'not to try to escape. My men are too busy to watch you and I would rather not put you in chains.'

"The three Americans looked at one another. What could they do? They had the word of the British Commander that they could soon go. They promised.

"Soon night came, and they could no longer see the shore.

" 'We're moving,' whispered Key.

" 'Where?' said Dr. Beanes.

"There was a great deal of activity on board. Soon Francis Key saw guns being fastened in their places on deck. Quick orders filled the air. Dim outlines of other boats were moving near by. They were all slipping like shadows through the quiet water.

" 'Fort McHenry,' said Key. 'They are headed

toward our fort. They're going to fire on Fort McHenry. How can we warn the fort?"

" 'We have given our word that we will not try to escape,' whispered Skinner.

"The three Americans hung over the rail, trying to see the shore. There was a whispered command. The gun at their side blazed.

"The rocket filled the air with sudden light. At once there was an answering shot from land.

" 'Apparently the fort has already been warned,' said Key.

" 'Thank God for that,' said Skinner.

"The fighting began in earnest. Back and forth flew the bombs. The night air was filled with shouts and screams.

"Suddenly in a brighter flash than usual, Mr. Key saw the stars and stripes of the American flag flying over the wall of the fort.

" 'Hurrah! Hurrah!' he shouted. 'The flag still waves. The Stars and Stripes is still there.' "

42

" 'Will she be in the morning?' said Dr. Beanes in a hoarse voice.

" 'Get back from that rail!' shouted a sailor. 'Don't you know we're fighting? You'll get hit.'

"But the three men stayed in their places. All night they strained their eyes. The hours went by. Wounded men were all about them. Several times they were ordered below deck but no one had time to see if they obeyed.

"Morning came, bringing first a little light and then the sun.

" 'It's there!' cried Key. "Hurrah! Hurrah! The flag is still there. Look! Look! See how it waves in the midst of the shells and the smoke!'

"The three men all shouted.

"Then Mr. Francis Scott Key took a pencil and an old envelope from his pocket.

"He began to write. He was writing the words to the song you sang today, Stevie. He was writing 'The Star-Spangled Banner.' "

For a minute no one spoke. Tray, as if he too knew that something thrilling had happened, put his paws on Stevie's knee.

"That's almost the best story I ever heard, Pa," said Mit.

"Me, too," said Dunning and Henry.

"Did Mr. Key and Mr. Skinner get to go back to the land?" asked Stevie.

"Yes. The very next morning the three Americans were put ashore, just as the British commander had said they would be. They hurried back to Baltimore. Mr. Key showed his new song to a relative, who had it printed.

"In a few days it was being sung on the streets. Everyone sang it. Everyone whistled it, too. Everyone liked it."

"Gee," said Dunning. "No wonder it's such an exciting song. Think of writing a song when the battle is going on all about you. 'Bombs bursting in air, gave proof through the night that our flag was still there.' Hurrah! Hurrah! for Mr. Francis Scott Key."

"Hurrah! Hurrah for our flag and Mr. Key!" said Stevie. "Let's sing it now. I like to sing it. Someday I'll write a song like 'The Star-Spangled Banner.'"

Everyone but Stevie's mother began to laugh. They all sang. One by one they stood up very straight. It was very exciting. Tray howled, too, and an owl near by began to hoot.

"Ma," said Stevie when he was in bed, "you think that I can write a song like 'The Star-Spangled Banner,' don't you?"

Mrs. Foster patted Stevie's cheek.

"Of course, dear," she answered.

I'll sing for you, play for you,

The Surprise Closet

DURING THE next two years Ann Eliza taught Stevie his letters and numbers, but what he liked to do best was to pick out tunes on her banjo and on the piano.

"He does mighty well," Lieve often said. "Just listen to that church tune he's playin'. I can sing right along with him."

"He has a fine ear for music," Mother Foster said. "But Mr. Foster wants him to think about other things he feels are more important."

"Miss Eliza, the songs he plays come right out of his heart," Lieve said once. "He plays just like my people sing. Mr. William's got no right

46

to stop my Stevie, and I'd like to tell him so, too."

In all the years since the war, none of the money which Pa had loaned to buy army supplies had been repaid. Stevie heard the grown-ups talking about "hard times." He wasn't interested in what the words meant until, one day, the piano was taken away.

"When will it be back, Ann Eliza?" he asked.

"It won't be back, Stevie," she said. "Ma sold it."

"Why? I want to play on it." Stevie ran to ask his mother.

"Stevie, when Pa's business is better I hope we can have a piano again," Ma said. "Right now we need the money, so I sold it."

Then one morning two wagons pulled up before the door and strange men carried the furniture from the house.

Stevie grabbed his little chair as one of the

men started to pick it up. "What are you doing? It's mine!"

"Stevie, we're moving to Harmony for a while," Ma explained. "Pa had to sell our house and the fields. But don't you worry. Pa's new business will soon be a success. Let the man have your chair, dear."

"I don't want to go away from here. I like my house," Stevie cried as he sat down on the steps. "Why do we have to go?"

The worst of the moving, however, came when Stevie learned that Lieve wasn't going with them. "Why?" he cried, hanging on to her arm. "I want my Lieve. I don't want to move."

"Don't you worry, Stevie. Lieve's goin' to rest a little spell. Then she's goin' to make cookies for her folks again," Lieve said.

The Fosters boarded in the near-by town and Stevie still had the banjo to play on. There were still stories in the evening, and the fall that

he was six he started to school with Mit. At first he was excited about school, but his excitement didn't last long. Dame Harvey, who had the school in her home, didn't understand this new boy.

"Stop looking out the window, Stephen. Keep your eyes on the primer," she would say as she tapped her ruler on her desk. "And don't ask what the words mean. Just read them!"

One morning the children read a story in their primer about a man who was burned at the stake. The picture in the primer showed flames rising up around the man as his family watched.

When he saw the picture, Stevie dropped his book. He stumbled over the other children's feet and ran from the school. He raced up the road with Mit after him. By the time he reached home he was crying.

"What is the matter, Stevie?" Ma asked.

"I don't like school," he said. "I don't want to

read about a man getting burned up. I want to stay home."

Mit returned to school, but Stevie had his wish. Ann Eliza taught him to read out of a song book. Stevie thought that was fun.

"This won't do," Pa said when he came home from Pittsburgh and heard what had happened. "What will Stephen amount to if he doesn't go to school with the other boys?"

"He can read better than Mit now, and Mit is nine years old, William," Ma said.

"I'll read you something funny, Pa," Stevie said, his eyes sparkling. "Listen:

"All around the old red barn,
The monkey chased the weasel,
Every time the monkey jumps
Pop goes the weasel.

"I can do it on the banjo, too, Pa," he added. "Do you want to hear me?"

"No. I simply won't have this," Pa said firmly.

"You must go to school like other boys. This music has to stop. Is that understood, Stephen? It has to stop!"

"Yes, sir," Stevie said.

Then the weather turned bad and both Stevie and Mit had to be kept at home. Ann Eliza taught them both. This was fun.

The Fosters lived in Harmony until Stevie was seven. Then they moved to a nice home of their own in Allegheny, Pennsylvania. Lieve came back and the cookies were the best ever.

One day when it was snowing very hard and the wind was blowing a gale, Stevie and Mit were in the kitchen with Mother and Lieve.

Lieve was making popcorn balls. Ma was mending the long black stockings which were worn by all her children. The fire in the big black stove crackled, and Tray crawled as close to its side as he could.

Steve and Mit stood looking out the window.

"This was just the kind of a day on which Grandpa Tomlinson was lost in the woods when he was a boy of your age, Stevie," said Mother.

"Was that the time the Indian chief found him and brought him home in the middle of the night?" asked Mit.

"Was that the time the Indian boy gave Grandpa Tomlinson the drum?" said Stevie.

"Yes. And that was the time the Indian gave Grandpa Tomlinson's mother the skin moccasins with the blue flower on the toe," said Ma. "The ones we keep in the Surprise Closet."

"Ma!" said Stevie. "Ma, may we have something out of the Surprise Closet? May we, Ma?"

"Please, Ma," shouted Mit. "I never did see what was in the Surprise Closet on the shelf right next to Pa's diary."

Mother Foster smiled and put her hand down into her apron pocket. She pulled out a bunch of large keys.

"It's just the day for the Surprise Closet, boys. It's a wonder I didn't think about it before. You can each bring out two things. Just *two,* mind you," said Ma.

"Hoop a la!" shouted Mit.

> "Yankee doodle, keep it up,
> Yankee doodle dandy:
> Mind the music and the step
> And with the girls be handy,"

sang Stevie.

He pulled a paper cap on his head and started to march around the kitchen.

Mit soon joined. Lieve pulled the pan of syrup to the back of the stove and followed. Ann Eliza and Etty came to see what was going on.

They all joined the fun. Stevie grabbed up a pan from the table and pounded on it with a wooden spoon as they marched around and around the kitchen. They were shouting "Yankee Doodle" as they went.

54

"Father and I went down to camp,
   Along with Captain Goodwin;
   And there we saw the men and boys
   As thick as hasty puddin'.

"Yankee doodle, keep it up,
   Yankee doodle dandy.
   Mind the music and the step
   And with the girls be handy."

Then out into the hall they trooped and right up to the closet under the stairs. Mit fitted the key into the door and opened it. The Surprise Closet was low and very dark.

"Just two things, now," said Ann Eliza. "That's what Ma said, Stevie."

It took a few seconds for their eyes to become used to the dark. As they peered into the exciting place they could see odd shapes of boxes, bags, and other things on the shelves.

It was here that mother kept all the special treasures of the family, things which the children could have only on days like this or when they were ill.

Half the fun of having the Surprise Closet was because it was so dark and spooky.

Mit took the diary from the top shelf. Then he lifted down the box which was placed just next to it.

Stevie pushed some old curtains aside and carefully lifted a guitar from the bottom shelf and an Indian drum from near by. Then he stood on tiptoe to take a slender package from above his head.

"Only two, Ma said so," insisted Mit.

"Oh, but I want——"

"Ma said only two."

"Then I'll take the guitar and Uncle Struthers' whistle," said Stevie. The whistle was in the small package.

Mit locked the door and everyone marched back into the kitchen.

56

Steve sat on the high stool and laid the guitar on the table.

"When you were only two, Stevie," said Mother Foster, "you used to lay that guitar on the floor and pick out tunes."

"You called it your 'ittly pizani," said Ann Eliza, smiling. "I guess you were trying to say little piano."

Stevie smiled. He began to pick out the tune which they had all been singing.

"You always seemed to know how to play the guitar and the piano, even without being taught," said Mother Foster. "I guess it just came natural to you."

"I can't play Uncle Struthers' whistle so well," said Stevie, taking it from the small package. "But I can make it sound out a little bit."

This was a small homemade instrument something like a flute. Stevie blew into one side near the very end. He also put his fingers up and down over the holes along the sides. There was a squeaky sound.

"I wish I could play like Uncle Struthers. Someday I want to go and visit Uncle Struthers on his farm. He asked me," said Stevie.

Uncle Struthers lived a long distance from Allegheny, but sometimes he visited the Foster family when he came east.

"The popcorn balls are all done," said Lieve. "They are mighty sticky, too."

Everyone left his treasures and rushed toward the stove. Lieve's popcorn balls were the best in the world. As soon as each had one Stevie began another march. Everyone joined in.

Nobody thought any more about the bad weather outside. It was such fun indoors.

Hard   Times, come a - gain   no   more.

Stevie Goes
with Lieve

Stevie sat on the piano stool and hummed a tune of his own. Then he picked out the tune with one finger. He touched the notes very lightly because the family were still asleep. It was very early on Sunday morning.

The piano was one which Brother William had sent to the family as a gift.

"Now that Stevie and Ann Eliza and Etty are all wanting to play, I think we should have a piano again," he had said to Mother Foster.

They had had a piano when they lived in the White Cottage in Pittsburgh, but it had cost too much to move it to Harmony.

For a while Mother Foster had tried to teach Stevie to play some of the music which lay on the piano.

"I don't want to practice," Stevie said. "I like to play the tunes that come into my head."

"That's better," said Pa. "Any kind of music is foolish for boys. The less time he spends on music the better."

So Ma didn't urge Stevie to practice, but he spent many hours sitting by the piano making up his own tunes and trying to play the ones that Lieve sang.

So early this Sunday morning, before the rest of the family were awake, he was humming a great favorite of hers. It was called "Little David."

"Little David, play on your harp, hallelu,
    hallelu,
Little David was a shepherd boy,
He killed Goliath and shouted for joy."

"It's too cold in here, Stevie," said Lieve from the door. "You better come in the kitchen with Lieve. I'm makin' corn bread."

Stevie hurried after her and climbed up on his favorite stool to watch her beat the batter and to hear her sing in time with the ringing of the spoon against the bowl.

"Let's sing 'All God's Chillun,' Lieve," he said. "I like that."

Lieve smiled and began to sway back and forth. The young colored girl always did this when she sang.

"You want to begin, Stevie?"

So Stevie began. He sang the words and Lieve the chorus. It was their singing, which soon grew very loud, which woke the family.

"I got a robe, you got a robe,
　All of God's chillun got a robe.
　When I get to heaven goin' to put on my robe,
　Goin' to shout all over God's heaven."

On and on they went. They sang another song and then another. The spoon rattled. Stevie beat his feet against the table and they both sang. It was lots of fun.

"Lieve! Stevie! I'm ready for my breakfast," said Pa's voice from the dining room. Breakfast wasn't ready.

"Yes, sir, Mister William," Lieve said. She rolled her eyes in such a funny way that Stevie began to giggle.

Then Lieve began to scurry about the kitchen. Pretty soon the whole family came down. They were all dressed in their Sunday clothes. They were going to church.

After breakfast Lieve beckoned to Stevie.

"Honey, you want to go with me to my church today?"

"With you to hear all the songs I like best?" shouted Stevie. "I'll go ask Ma."

Mother Foster was sitting very primly in the

parlor. She didn't mend or sew or knit on Sunday. She was waiting for Pa to bring around the carriage.

Stevie leaned against her knees and asked if he might go with Lieve. Ma looked surprised.

"But Stevie, we want you to go with us. Why do you want to go with Lieve?"

"Because I want to hear all her friends sing the songs I like best," Stevie answered.

"But we don't go to church to hear the singing. We go to hear the minister and to pray."

"Please, Ma," urged Stevie. "Please."

So, an hour later, Stevie and Lieve started off in the deep snow to the little frame church down by the river.

When they arrived, people were hurrying inside the church. Lieve spoke to everyone as she walked down the aisle. Stevie hung close to her skirts. He was used to her kind face, but there were many strangers here.

They all smiled at the little white boy. Stevie
sat next to an old, old woman who was too crip-
pled to stand up when everyone else did. She
kept her eyes closed most of the time but she
repeated all the words which the others spoke.

64

"When will they start to sing, Lieve?" Stevie whispered.

"Pretty soon, honey. Just you wait. There goes the minister right now."

Everyone but the little old woman stood up. Everyone bowed his head. The minister began to pray. It was a very long prayer. Stevie tried to keep his eyes closed, but it was hard. He peeped a little. He watched the others about him.

They seemed so poor. It was a very cold day, and yet many of them were without warm coats. But they looked happy as they mumbled some of the prayer with the minister.

Suddenly a woman up near the front of the room began to sing.

> "Oh, the river of Jordan is so wide,
> One more river to cross.
> One more river to cross.
> I don't know how to get on the other side,
> One more river to cross."

The congregation began to sing.

"Hallelujah, Hallelujah, Hallelujah,
Praise the Lord. Praise the Lord."

Then the woman sang another verse and the people sang the chorus. Stevie looked at Lieve. She had her eyes closed. He couldn't ask, so he began to sing, too. He loved to sing.

They sang several of his favorite songs. There was the one called "Swing Low, Sweet Chariot." Another was called "Steal Away to Jesus."

The congregation sang these very softly. Stevie found that he had tears in his eyes just as had the old woman next to him.

After church he and Lieve ran most of the way home. They were there before the family. Stevie stood before the kitchen fire and got warm.

"Lieve," he said after a while, "are the songs which you and all your friends sing written down in Ma's music book?"

66

"No, Stevie. My songs are in my heart, right about here. My Grandmammy and Pappy taught me my songs, honey."

"I like them best," said Stevie. "They make my throat feel queer but I like them. Listen, I'll play 'Steal Away to Jesus' for you right now."

When Pa and Ma and the family came in Stevie and Lieve were at the piano. Pa frowned.

"Mother," he said, "Stephen is to go back to school. I can't have all this music and singing. He's past six now. He must learn to do sums and to spell."

Stevie heard his father. He slipped quietly from the room and hurried over to where Mit was playing with Tray. They both played with the dog until dinner was ready.

Old   dog   Tray's   ev - er   faith - ful,

Jake Plays
the Banjo

WHEN STEVIE was seven he and Ma and Pa were visiting in Pittsburgh. They were staying with friends whom they had known when they lived in the White Cottage.

Today they had come downtown in a hired hack. Pa had some business to attend to. Ma was going to do some shopping. Stevie was going to look around. He liked that.

"Now," said Pa, "I'll leave you two here. I'll come for you in three hours. Will that be time enough for you, my dear?"

Ma smiled. She stepped carefully from the hack to the high walk. The streets were very muddy in Pittsburgh. Stevie jumped down after her. Pa waved to them and was soon gone.

"Stevie," said Ma, "I'm going into this store. You may go anywhere you like as long as you stay on this street."

Stevie nodded. Ma disappeared through the store door. Stevie was by himself. He looked about to see what to do first.

There, right across the street, was a great covered wagon, a Conestoga wagon. Four brown oxen were hitched to it. A man with a red beard rode on a white horse beside them. Stevie knew now what he wanted to do.

He picked his way through the mud that almost covered his high buttoned shoes. He had always wanted to see inside a covered wagon.

Stevie saw a boy lean forward from the front seat of the wagon.

"You stay here with the wagon, Bud," said the man on the horse. "We'll bring you some bullets for your new gun. You just keep your eye on everything here."

The boy grinned and pulled off his wide-brimmed hat. He wiped his hot face on his sleeve. A tall woman and a little girl climbed out of the back of the wagon. Everyone left but Bud.

Stevie stood near the big front wheel. "Hello," he said.

"Hello," said the big boy. "Hello, Bud."

"My name isn't Bud," said Stevie. "I thought that was your name."

"My name's David," said the boy. "Jake just calls me Bud. What's your name?"

"Stephen Foster."

The two boys looked at each other.

"Want to come up and sit a spell while Pop's gone?" said David. "I got a new gun I can show you."

Stevie climbed up on the axle of the great wooden wheel.

70

"Here, I'll give you a hand," said David. "You ain't much bigger than Effie."

"Who's Effie?" asked Stevie.

"My sister. She just went off with Mom."

"Oh," said Stevie.

Then neither spoke. David was looking at the gun which lay across his knees. Stevie waited. David began to rub the barrel of the gun with some rags.

"Where are you going?" Stevie asked finally.

"Indiany," said David.

"Is that far?" asked Stevie.

"Yep."

"Can you shoot?" asked Stevie.

"Sure," said David.

Stevie began to look about him. It was almost dark inside the wagon, but he could see the outline of furniture, barrels, boxes, and some clothes hanging up on the braces of the canvas cover. It was lighter toward the back.

Stevie started to climb into the wagon.

"Where you goin'?" said David. "Pop wouldn't want strangers in there."

"I want to see that banjo that's hanging up in there. Is it yours?"

"Nope, that's Jake's."

"Who's Jake?" asked Stevie.

"Say, you're a great one for asking questions, ain't you?" said David.

Stevie waited. He wondered if David would answer his last question.

"Jake's the man that's ridin' with us. He sure can make that banjo play," said David.

"What does he play? What kind of tunes, I mean," Stevie asked.

"Lots of tunes," said David. "He plays when we settle down for the night. It's mighty comfortin' then, too."

"Comforting?" said Stevie.

"Don't you know nothing, Bud?" said David.

72

"Comfortin' makes you feel safer—like when it's lonesome."

Stevie understood. He was sorry he had asked. He changed the subject. "Is it fun riding to Indiany?" he asked.

"Sometimes. It's mighty cold nights. There might be Indians out west. Jake says there's some in Indiany."

Stevie turned to look at the oxen. He wished Jake would come. Maybe he would play a tune for him. "Do you ride all night?" he asked.

"No," said David.

"What if Indians are around? What do you do then?" Stevie went on.

"Shoot 'em before they shoot us."

For a minute Stevie was quiet. He looked again back into the wagon.

"I wish Jake would play his banjo when he comes. Will he?"

"Maybe. Jake's the best player in these parts.

He takes all the prizes. You can't keep your feet still when Jake plays."

"Here comes your father," said Stevie suddenly. "Is that Jake?"

"Sure. Sure," said David. "That's Jake and my uncle and Pop and Mom and Effie. I guess we'll be goin' now."

"Can I ask Jake to play?" said Stevie.

David didn't answer. He had jumped down and was helping lift a large box into the back of the wagon. Stevie heard him say, "That boy up in front is Stephen, Pop. He wanted to see Jake's banjo. I didn't let him."

Stevie's face flushed. He started to get down. No one was paying any attention to him. He turned and was ready to climb over the wheel when he heard a new voice.

"Do you play the banjo, son?"

"No, sir," said Stevie.

The man who was standing by him was very

tall. His eyes were blue. He smiled broadly.
"Want to hear Mamie play, do you?" he asked.

"Mamie?" said Stevie.

"My banjo. All good banjos has names, son.
Jest like people. Mamie's the best little gal in
these parts."

"Will you—make her sing?" asked Stevie. "I'd
like to hear her."

Jake threw back his head and laughed and
laughed. "Bust my strings I will," he said.
"Come on, young 'un. I'll show you how Mamie
kin sing."

Jake took the banjo from its peg. He patted it
and blew on the strings and wiped off the dust
with his sleeve.

"What'll it be, son?" he said.

Stevie shook his head. He was so excited he
couldn't speak.

Jake began to play. People on the street
stopped walking and came over to the wagon.

David was right. No one could keep his feet still when Jake played.

Jake sang, too. It was a song Stevie had never heard. It was a lively dancing song. Then, with another tune, he made Mamie cry. Then he played "Hail, Columbia" and everyone sang.

When Jake played, Stevie could almost feel how lonely it was out on the way to Indiana.

"Don't know how we'd make it without Mamie," said Jake. "She'll have to hang up till night now, though. We gotta be goin'. Here comes the missus."

It took a very short time for all David's family to climb into the great covered wagon.

Stevie hurried around to the front of the wagon to say good-by. But David was looking toward the west and Indiana.

"Good-by," Stevie shouted.

David didn't turn.

The wagon rumbled off down the street. Jake

sprang onto his white horse. He rode by the side of the oxen. He carried a long whip which he circled over their backs.

"See you in Indiany!" he shouted.

Stevie waved. The wagon rounded the corner and was gone. The crowd was soon gone, too. Stevie crossed the street and began to look into the store windows.

"I wish I could make up a song like those that Jake plays," he said to himself.

The sound of Jake's music was still ringing in Stevie's ear, when he heard another kind of music. It came from farther down the street.

"I wonder who's playing the piano on this street?" said Stevie to himself.

He hurried down the board walk and saw a crowd of men standing in the doorway of a small shop called the Smith and Mellon's Music Shop. The music was coming from just beyond the men. Stevie pushed his way under their arms.

78

There he saw a strange sight, and he heard a salesman say, "It's the first upright piano ever to be seen outside of Philadelphia. My friend John Isaac Hawkins invented it."

"Who's he?" asked one of the men.

"He's an Englishman who lives in Philadelphia. The pianos we've had before take up so much room when they're moved. This one can easily be sent in a Conestoga wagon or by barge on the river."

"It sounds just the same as a piano to me," said Stevie.

No one had noticed him before. He stood near the instrument.

"May I play it a little?" he asked.

"Certainly not," said the young salesman. "It's valuable. It belongs to Henry Kleber, the musician. He wouldn't want you banging on it."

"But I wouldn't bang," Stevie said. "I just want to see how——"

"No, run along now, sonny. Where's your mother?" said another man.

"But I can play it. Please let me," said Stevie.

But the men pushed him away. Stevie looked about him as he walked toward the door. There were many musical instruments in cases. Among others there was a banjo and a violin. Right on the front counter was something which Stevie had never seen before.

It was small and black. It looked a little like Uncle Struthers' whistle. Stevie stopped and stood on tiptoe. No one was watching him now. Everyone had gone back to look at the upright piano again.

Stevie took the small instrument into his hands and held it carefully. He lifted it to his mouth. There was a small hole near the end, just as there was on Uncle Struthers' instrument. Stevie blew into this. There was a sweet sound.

He pressed his fingers over the holes which

were cut into the side. The sound changed. He blew softly again. It was a tune.

Stevie forgot that he was in a store and that the man who had tried to put him out would probably do so again. He played a little louder. He began to play one of his favorite tunes. It was "Hail, Columbia."

"Here, here! What are you doing back in this store?" said the young storekeeper. "Go along. Put that flageolet down."

"Don't bother the lad, Burnes," said a new voice. "He is remarkable."

"But Mr. Kleber, that is our best——"

"Shaw! Let the boy alone."

Stevie heard the men talking. He was glad that the taller man was the boss. He played on and on. The men gathered about him. Stevie liked this. He liked to have people listen to him.

Then he heard his mother's voice.

"Stevie," she said, "you must come now."

"But madam," said his new friend, "your boy is truly remarkable. He must take many lessons. I myself will teach him."

"I'm afraid not," said Mother Foster. "His father has other plans for him. Come, Stevie."

"Oh, Ma," said Stevie. "May I have this? May I, Ma?"

"Of course he must have the flageolet, Madam," said the older musician. "He is gifted beyond anyone of his age whom I have ever heard."

Mother Foster was very pleased. She thought quickly. The Fosters had very little money. She decided that she really could wear her old, old dress again so that she might buy the little flute for Stevie.

When they left the store Stevie carried the treasure with him.

When they were joined by Mr. Foster, Stevie showed him the flageolet. He began to play a

82

lively little tune for his father. His father was very angry.

"I simply won't have it, my dear," he said. "I've told you before, music is not for boys. Put it away, Stevie."

Stevie was disappointed. He put the new gift back into its box.

"Pa," he said, "Mr. Kleber, at the music store, had a new kind of piano, too. It looks like a box. It stands up instead of lying down. It was made by a man in Philadelphia whose name is Mr. Hawkins. Maybe I could make a new kind of a piano someday."

"Now you see, my dear," said Pa. "He thinks of nothing but music. I doubt if he ever heard of Robert Fulton and his steamboat the 'Clermont.' Did you, Stevie?"

Stevie shook his head.

"But William, the boy is only seven. He isn't very grown-up yet," said Ma.

"But he knows how to play the flute and he knows who made the newest type of piano," said Mr. Foster.

Mother Foster didn't answer. The trip home to Allegheny was a very quiet one. But Stevie didn't mind. He had his new flageolet, and that was enough to make any boy happy.

What must a fai - ry's dream be,

Exciting News

STEVIE STOPPED short. He was carrying in the wood for Lieve's stove when he heard Ma and Pa talking. He heard Ma say, "I'll take Stevie and Etty with me, William. It will be good for both of them."

"What will be good for me?" said Stevie from the door.

"Stephen, were you listening?" asked Pa.

"No, I was just bringing in the wood for Lieve. What would be good for Etty and me?"

"How would you like to take a long ride in a river boat, Stevie?" said Ma.

"To stay on it at night?" asked Stevie.

"Yes, for several nights," said Ma. "Would you like that?"

"Hurrah! Hurrah!" shouted Stevie. "Etty! Etty! Come here. Come here."

Etty came running. "Whatever's the matter, Stevie? Are you hurt?"

"What's the matter, Stevie?" said Lieve. "What's the matter, honey?"

"Nothing. Nothing," said Stevie. "We're going on a river boat. We're going on a river boat."

Stevie began to march about the room singing,

> "We're going on a river boat,
> We're going on a river boat,
> We're going on a river boat
> In the morning."

Suddenly he stopped. "What's the name of the boat, Pa?" he asked.

"The 'Napoleon,'" said Pa. "It leaves on Wednesday. You're going 'way down to Augusta, Kentucky, to visit Uncle Joseph."

Stevie shouted:

"The 'Napoleon,' 'Napoleon.'
We're going on a river boat
And her name is called 'Napoleon.'"

Around and around the room Stevie marched, shouting and singing his gay little song.

Wednesday was very near, and there was a great deal to be done before then.

"Lieve," said Mamma, "will you get out all of Stevie's clothes? They must be washed."

Lieve smiled. Then she looked at Stevie. "How am I going to get along without my Stevie?" she said.

"What's Mit going to do, Mamma? Can't he go with us?" said Etty.

"He and Dunning will go to work this summer," Ma said.

So the plans were made. The day came closer and closer. Stevie spent most of the time down by the wharf watching the boats dock. One day

87

he saw Ned, his friend who on his fourth birth-day had taught him to fish.

"I'm going to take a trip on the 'Napoleon,' Ned," he said.

"Where's Mister Stevie goin'?"

"Down to Augusta, Kentucky," said Stevie.

"Down in old Kentucky! Why, honey, that's where my folks live."

"I didn't know you had a family, Ned," said Stevie. "Tell me about them."

"My white family, honey," said Ned. "Old Ned ran away 'cause Old Master died and Ned didn't want to be sold."

"Sold, Ned?" said Stevie. "What do you mean? How could you be sold?"

"I was a slave, Mister Stevie. Didn't you know that?"

"A slave? What's a slave?"

"I don't rightly know, honey," Ned answered, "only I was a slave. When my good old master

89

died, then all the Negro folks got sold. So Ned ran away."

That night Stevie was very quiet. He sat looking at his supper instead of eating it. He wasn't singing and marching as he had been every other night since he knew he was going on the trip.

"Aren't you hungry, Stevie?" asked Pa.

"No, sir," said Stevie. "Papa, is Lieve a slave?"

"What put that in your head, son?"

Stevie told him what Ned had said.

"You wouldn't sell Lieve, would you, Pa?"

"No, Stevie, indeed I wouldn't. But don't you worry your head about such things as slavery. There's many a grown-up head that's going to worry over that."

"But you're sure you won't sell Lieve?"

"Sure, Stevie. I wouldn't think of it. Now run to bed. Remember, tomorrow you and Mother and Etty are leaving. Get a good sleep."

Stevie climbed slowly up the stairs. Lieve was in his room fixing his bed. He ran to her and threw his arms about her waist.

"Lieve, Lieve, don't you worry. Pa says he won't ever sell you. He promised."

Lieve looked surprised. She gave Stevie a big hug and went singing down the stairs.

Stevie undressed as quickly as he could. He wanted tomorrow to come as fast as it could. He sang as he hopped into bed. Lieve was safe and he was going on the riverboat in the morning.

> "We're going on the riverboat,
> We're going on the riverboat,
> We're going on the riverboat,
> In the morning,"

he sang as his eyes grew heavy.

"Riverboat, riverboat——" Suddenly Stevie was asleep.

Papa took Mrs. Foster, Stevie, and Etty down to the boat. Stevie hopped up and down on the wharf. He wanted to run and hunt for Ned. But Ma held onto his hand.

Etty was trying to be very grown-up. Her dress was new. She had her hair fixed in a snood. Her little hat made her look like a grown-up young lady.

Etty was fifteen now and no longer wanted to play games. Stevie, who was just seven, missed his playmate.

When the "Napoleon" docked, Captain Stone was in the wheelhouse. He saw Mr. Foster and waved to him. As soon as the boat was tied up to the wharf he came down to talk to Stevie's father.

"This," said William Foster, "is Mrs. Foster, sir. She and our two children, Henrietta and Stephen, are going with you on this trip."

"That will be a pleasure, Mrs. Foster," said the Captain. "And I hope that you will do me the honor of sitting at my table."

Stevie and Etty looked at each other. They

didn't know just what this meant but it was going to be fun. They were sure of that.

Pa stood on the wharf until the "Napoleon" was far away down the river. Stevie and Etty waved and waved. When they could no longer see Pa they started down to find Ma. She was already in the little room where they were to sleep. It was called a cabin.

The steps down which they were hurrying were broad. Everything was painted white—the walls, the railing, the chairs on the deck. There were colored boys hurrying about carrying trays of things to eat.

Stevie's eyes opened wide. He looked down another flight of steps. At the foot he could see more colored boys lugging and rolling great boxes and barrels across the floor.

"Etty, let's go see what's in those boxes," said Stevie.

"No, we promised Ma we would come right

down to the cabin. Come on. You can ask questions later on."

So the two went along the deck to a small slatted door. Inside they found Ma trying to put their things away into the very small space in which they were to live for three days.

"Is that where I'm going to sleep, up there?" said Stevie.

He pointed to a narrow bunk which was fastened over another just as narrow which was lower down.

"No, you and I will sleep in the lower one, Stevie. Etty will climb up above."

"Oh, why can't I be up high? I can climb much better than Etty can."

"Let him, Ma," said Etty. "I don't think I'd like it up there."

"But Stevie is smaller. The bed is very narrow. I think he had better be down with me."

"Well anyhow," said Stevie starting for the

door, "I'm going down to see what's in the boxes and barrels they are loading across the deck."

"Don't climb up on the rail," called Ma. But Stevie didn't hear her. He was leaning as far across the rail as he could.

"There's another boat passing us," he shouted.

As the two boats passed, everyone shouted. Suddenly Stevie heard the music of several banjos. The sound came from below. Stevie ran for the steps and hurried down to the cargo deck.

The barrels and boxes were piled at one end of the space. Stevie's eyes sparkled. Two tall lanky colored boys were dancing in the center of the floor. Several others lolled on the boxes playing the banjos Stevie had heard. An old man sat with his fiddle tucked under his chin.

> "How does the water flow?
> How does the water go?
> Rollin'—rollin',"

sang the old man.

"Rollin' . . . rollin' . . . rollin',"

shouted the dancers.

"How does the whistle blow?
How does the whistle blow?
Blow—blow—blow,"

sang the fiddler.

"Blow—blow—blow,"

shouted the other men.

Stevie hurried around the side of the floor and sat down by the musicians. He clapped his hands as they did. He sang with them, too. He smiled and they smiled back at him.

Stevie knew that he was going to like this trip down the Ohio.

The Glen-dy Burke has a fun-ny old crew

Wandering Stevie

THE FIRST night that Stevie was on board the "Napoleon," there was moonlight. Mother Foster, Etty and Stevie sat on the upper deck. They were watching the shadows and listening to the strange noises which come to a riverboat in the evening.

"Is the Ohio a very deep river?" asked Stevie.

"Yes, it is in lots of places. Why, Stevie?" said Ma.

"I just wondered. Lieve has a song she sings about the Jordan River. It's a deep river, too."

Several young ladies and gentlemen were walking about the deck in the moonlight. Their

97

voices carried up to where Stevie sat. The boat creaked and shivered as it pushed along through the water. Sometimes there were voices on shore. From around the bend came the sound of band music. Stevie ran to the rail.

The "Napoleon" slowed down. Her whistle blew twice. She was answered from beyond.

"We must be going to pass another boat," said Mother. "If it's on this side we'll be able to see all the people on it because just here the river isn't very wide."

"Is that band on the other boat, do you think?" asked Stevie.

"I think it is," said Ma.

Many other passengers crowded close to the Fosters as they leaned against the rail. Suddenly, out of the darkness, there came a glare of light. It was moving toward them.

"It's a fire!" shrieked Stevie. "It's a fire, Ma!"

Everyone about them laughed. A tall man

picked Stevie up and put him on his shoulder. "There, young man, shout hello to the 'Golden Belle,' the finest boat on the river. Listen to the song they're playing on that top deck."

> "Should auld acquaintance be forgot,
> And never brought to mind?
> Should auld acquaintance be forgot,
> And the days of auld Lang Syne."

The people on both boats sang, and the bells on both boats rang. Everyone waved. The "Napoleon" and the "Golden Belle" passed each other. Then the music became fainter. The lights disappeared. The sound of the water splashing over the paddle wheel came again. Owls hooted at each other and the crickets on the shore chirped and chirped.

Stevie leaned far over the rail. The water looked very black. Up near the prow it foamed and rushed like ruffles of white silk.

"Come," said Ma. "Off to bed so that you can

get up early in the morning to see what happens on a big riverboat."

Before Stevie was quite asleep, he leaned out of the door of the cabin. The moon was riding high. The deep Ohio was carrying them down, down between its high banks.

Somewhere on shore men were singing.

"Comin' for to carry me home."

Stevie tumbled into bed.

"Swing low, sweet chariot,
Comin' for to carry me home,"

came the music. It was far off now. Stevie was asleep.

Early the next morning Stevie woke with a start. The "Napoleon" had stopped. He heard shouts from outside. He climbed quickly out of his bunk, pulled on his clothes, and ran out on the deck. As he ran he bumped straight into Captain Stone.

"Good morning, young man," said the Captain. "Where are you going so fast?"

"I just want to see everything. I guess I slept too late."

"Oh, we just came into this wharf. Would you like to go ashore with me?"

"Oh, I would, I would," said Stevie.

"Come along then," said the Captain. "I want to see some men. Will you stay right close to me and not run away?"

"Yes, sir," said Stevie. "I just want to see what all that pounding and shouting is about."

The two hurried down the wide steps. They went through the cargo room.

"Look out, there, Captain," shouted a young Negro boy suddenly. "That barrel of molasses is loose."

Stevie and Captain Stone jumped back just in time.

"I'm sorry, Mister Captain," said the boy. "I'm

very sorry. That barrel just up and rolled right off my stick, it did."

"Look over there, Stevie," said his new friend. "See those boys backing down the hill? Watch them. See how they roll those great barrels of molasses down to the boat?"

The two walked over the gangplank. Stevie hopped by the tall Captain's side. This was the most exciting time he had ever known. Everyone was shouting. Women carried great baskets of fruit and vegetables on their heads.

Before them Stevie saw big strong colored boys bending their backs under the weight of the load they were supporting.

"What are they doing there?" Stevie asked.

"That is the only way they know to get those barrels down the hill. Stand back here and watch. Look at the top of the hill. See that group of men carrying their barrel off the wagon? Now watch," said Captain Stone.

Carefully the men turned the barrel so that the rolling side was toward the hill which led to the gangplank.

As it was turned, two men pushed along spade-like sticks with thin edges under the staves. They braced themselves and then let the barrel roll a very little way.

Then two more men slipped their spades under the side and the heavy weight rolled again. So they came, a little bit at a time.

"Easy, boys," shouted the foreman. "Slow, slow, slow."

"If one of those great barrels got away and went crashing down the hill it might kill several men before it could be stopped," said Captain Stone. "The men have to be careful."

Stevie followed the Captain in and out among the crowd. He listened and looked. He hoped that there would be some dancing and playing on the levee, but everyone was too busy.

It was breakfast time when Stevie and the Captain reached the boat again. All that day and the next Stevie wandered about the "Napoleon." No one seemed to mind. People liked the little boy who asked so many questions.

The boat docked at Augusta, Kentucky, on the fourth night. Mother's brother, Joseph Tomlinson, met the Fosters and took them up to his house.

Mr. Tomlinson was the president of a college. He and Mother Foster and all the older people had a very gay time during their visit. Etty met young people whom she liked and she went to parties, too.

Stevie just wandered wherever he wished. It was lots of fun.

"He is too young to be about among strangers alone," said Ma to Uncle Joseph.

"Not at all, my dear," said Mr. Tomlinson. "At least not down here on the plantation. All the colored folks love children. He'll learn a lot by just going about as he pleases."

So it was arranged. Stevie was free to go where he liked all day long. Sometimes he didn't come in for dinner. It was fun eating in the fields with some of the men.

On the plantation next to his uncle's, tobacco was raised. Stevie was excited about this. The great fields seemed endless to Stevie.

The first time that Stevie touched one of the large drooping leaves of the tobacco plant he pulled his hand back quickly. His fingers were covered with something gummy and cold.

"It feels better when the leaves are dry, Mister Stevie," said an old colored man. "Here, let old Mose wipe off your hand."

"What are the men doing in all those rows?" Stevie asked.

"We're cuttin', honey. We're cuttin' the best crop in the whole state of Kentucky. Just you

106

look at that big green leaf. Mighty soon old sun's goin' to dry that leaf all brown."

"Then what do you do with it, Uncle Mose?" asked Stevie.

"Then we're goin' to stack it nice-like in the barn till it's dry. And then, after the rain comes and the stems get all soft again, Uncle Mose is goin' to strip the leaves off the stems and tie 'em up in bunches big as my arms," said the old man.

"And then?" asked Stevie.

"Then they're goin' to be packed in nice piles and Old Marse'll sell the piles. The best tobacco in all Kentucky comes from Rosemount, this here plantation."

"Is it ready to use then, Uncle Mose?"

"No, honey, it's got to stand maybe one, maybe two-three years first. Then it's goin' to taste mighty sweet in folks' pipes and cigars," answered the old man.

That evening Stevie went with Uncle Mose to

his little cabin, which was built back of the big house. There were many little cabins there. Many little colored children played near by.

Stevie stayed until the moon came up. Then he heard all the slaves singing. They seemed happy, but their songs were mournful. Stevie never forgot that night.

He never forgot all the days of the weeks that he visited Uncle Joseph in Augusta.

When he and Etty and Ma reached home in Harmony, he tried to sing the tunes to Lieve. He tried to play them on the piano. Then he tried to make up some songs which would sound like those he heard before Uncle Mose's cabin. It was the middle of the summer when he came home. Stevie talked about the trip to everyone.

Old songs! new songs! ev'ry kind of song,

Mr. Kelly
of Dublin

It HAD BEEN two years since the wonderful trip to Augusta. Stevie was nine and Mit was twelve.

Dunning and Henry were no longer going to school. They were working. Mit was to go to the Allegheny Academy. Stevie was happy because he was to stay home again this winter. It cost too much to send both boys.

Then a letter came. Stevie saw Pa take it from his pocket. It was the night before school was to open.

"My dear," said Pa to Mother, "Stevie is to have a chance to go to school with Morrison. Young William will send us the money."

"But, Pa," said Stevie, "I don't want to go. Please, Pa. I'll study hard at home."

"No, my son," said Father Foster. "You must begin to think of what you'll do for a living. School is the best place to learn that."

So the next day Stevie went with Mit.

He was never sorry that he did, because it was here in Dr. Stockton's school, called Allegheny Academy, that he grew to know Mr. John Kelly.

On the very first day the boys came into Mr. Kelly's room, they liked him. When the class gathered he was standing looking out of the window. "Good morning, young gentlemen," he said. "I see it's an exceptionally fine morning. I suggest we finish our figures and reading lesson as quickly as we can. Then there will be more time for a game of ball."

The boys looked at one another. They smiled at Mr. Kelly. He smiled at them and they all began to work.

110

"I have a letter to write," Mr. Kelly went on. "I'll be busy, too."

The room was very quiet that morning. It was always quiet when Mr. Kelly was there. Other teachers couldn't understand it. "And he doesn't use the whip, either," an older one said.

One day when they were all out playing "catch," and Stevie was sitting on the fence watching, Mr. Kelly called to him. "Come,

Stevie, you can catch a ball as well as you catch a tune, and that's better than any of us."

The boys all laughed. But they were not laughing *at* Stevie, they were laughing *with* him.

Another day, when the other classes had been very unruly, the teachers told Mr. Kelly, "You'll have trouble today, John."

Mr. Kelly shook his head. Then he wrote a few words on bits of paper and put them on the desks. "Work hard so that you can play hard—that's a gentleman's way," the message said.

Sometimes Mr. Kelly took Stevie for long walks along the river. Then he told him about his old home in Dublin, Ireland.

"I'm Irish, praise be! Dublin is a grand city. You should hear the music of the Irish harp."

"Is it like a flute or a piano?"

"It has strings like a banjo and the sounds of angels singing come from them. Ah, the music played in Ireland comes from the heart, lad."

"Like the music the colored folks sing?"

"A little. Yes, more than a little," said Mr. Kelly, and he wiped the tears from his eyes.

Stevie understood how Mr. Kelly felt about music like this. He did, too, when he went to church with Lieve.

Stevie did very well in school this year. All the boys did. Mr. Kelly was a fine teacher and a friend to his pupils.

Stevie was so happy in this school that he really wanted to learn. A long time after Stephen left Mr. Kelly and the academy he wrote a poem which he called the "Old School Master." It was a tribute to his good friend.

These were the happiest school days that Stephen Foster ever spent.

Long live the merry, merry heart That laughs by night and day,

Minstrels
Are Coming

ONE DAY old Ned told Stevie and Mit the best minstrel show in the world was coming to town. The three of them were fishing from the wharf.

"It come today," he went on. "I gotta find me a ticket. You all goin'?"

The boys jumped to their feet. Last year the Fosters were visiting when this show came, but they had heard about it from the boys.

"Yes, we are," Stevie said.

"Tickets cost money, Stevie," said Mit. "But if we think hard maybe we can figure a way to buy some. Boys carried the signs through the streets last year for tickets. I could do that."

114

"So could I," said Stevie.

"No, you couldn't. They're awful heavy," Mit sad, and Ned nodded. Stevie was tall but not very strong in his arms.

"Just you wait. I'll find a way," Stevie said with a frown. He pushed his cap back. "I know. I'll ask Mr. Kelly to let me weed his garden. He'd much rather read or take a walk than do that. I think he would pay me." Stevie ran all the way to the school.

"Mr. Kelly! Mr. Kelly!" he called.

Mr. Kelly put his head out the window. "Hello, Stevie, my lad. What may I do for you?"

"Mr. Kelly, the minstrels are coming to town and I just have to go. Could I weed your garden?"

"What has weeding my garden to do with a minstrel show?" Mr. Kelly laughed, but Stevie knew he understood and was joking.

"Well, weeding a garden isn't so easy," Stevie

115

went on, "and besides, you could take a walk or maybe read or——"

"Would a ticket to the show pay you?" Mr. Kelly asked, and the two of them laughed.

When the doors to the hall opened that night, Stevie and Mit were the first boys inside.

"My, that sign was heavy!" whispered Mit.

"My back's pretty sore. So are my hands."

Then they began to grin.

"The show's going to start," said Stevie. "Look at the curtains move. The actors are getting settled in their places."

The curtains were pulled aside. There were fifteen men on stage, all dressed in fancy suits. They had their faces painted black. Each one had a white line of paint about his red mouth.

The head man in the show was called the "in-ter-loc-u-tor."

"He asks all the questions when the time comes," whispered Stevie.

Then the show began. There were banjos to strum, bones to rattle, a tambourine to shake, and Mr. Interlocutor to play the fiddle. At first everyone played at once. They all kept time with their feet. Each seemed to be trying to make more noise than all the rest.

The audience began to sing and clap and stamp their feet. Stevie and Mit clapped and shouted as loud as the others. After this part of the show was over, Mr. Interlocutor asked funny questions and riddles.

The show was a great success. The boys wanted to see another right away.

"Why don't we?" said Stevie. "We could give as good a show as they can. That is—almost as good. We could charge for it and spend the money for tickets to go and see Daddy Rice in Pittsburgh."

Daddy Rice was the greatest and most popular minstrel of the day.

The boys were so excited that they could hardly wait until the next day to get started.

"Come and see the biggest show on earth! Come one, come all! Step right up and get your tickets now! Just a few seats left."

It was Mit shouting outside the Fosters' carriage house.

He wore a high hat, borrowed from Mr. Cuddy, one of the teachers, and his face was rubbed with burnt cork.

Stevie peeped out from behind the curtain. "The seats up in front are all full," he whispered. "Mr. Kelly's on the front row." Stevie wore Mr. Kelly's high hat.

There were only nine boys in the company. But the stage was arranged as the big minstrel show had been. Boxes were placed in a semi-

118

circle, and each boy sat behind a box. Mit was the interlocutor, Stevie the soloist.

"Are you ready?" whispered the youngest Cuddy boy. "My father just came in. He brought four people with him."

Some of the boys had dishpans and spoons. Some had stones that rattled in pans. Stevie had his flute and banjo and the whistle which Ned had made him.

The curtain was made of two carriage robes. "Be careful when you pull it," whispered Mit. It moved jerkily and stopped. "Look out," Mit muttered. "It's stuck."

The audience knew that there was something wrong. There was tittering from the back row.

"Pull again," said Mit.

"It won't pull," said Ben. "What'll we do?"

Stevie stood near by with the banjo in his hands. His face was corked. The white line about his red lips was crooked and his hat, Mr.

Kelly's hat, came almost to his ears. "Wait a minute," he whispered. "I'll go out before the curtain. Then you can fix it."

The audience began to call. They began to clap. They began to whistle. Then they began to laugh. They laughed harder. Some shouted.

They were watching a small figure who hobbled across the stage. He pulled his hat down farther and made a deep bow. Then he started to dance. He danced and he pranced. Then he sang.

Gradually the crowd quieted down. The song was different from those usually heard in a minstrel. It went:

> "I got shoes;
> You got shoes;
> All of God's Chillun got shoes."

The audience was still now.

"It's all fixed," came a loud whisper from behind the scenes.

120

The little figure bowed and backed off the stage. Stevie had saved the day. Everyone shouted and cheered.

"Send him back again," they cried.

Stevie came out for another bow. His hat slipped off and the audience saw who it was.

"Stevie!" they shouted. "Stevie Foster."

Ma and Pa were near the front of the house. They felt very proud.

The show went on with dances and songs. Then came the riddles which the boys had worked up for themselves.

Mit, the interlocutor, stepped forward. All the cast sat in a semicircle.

"You, Mr. Bones," said Mit. "Why ain't you ever goin' to starve on the desert of Arabia when you get there?"

"Why ain't I never goin' to starve on the desert of Arabia, Mr. Interlocutor? Let me see. 'Deed, I don't know."

"You ain't goin' to starve, Mr. Bones, 'cause of all the sand which is there."

"Sandwiches there—get it?" said somebody in the front row. Everybody laughed.

"It worked," whispered Stevie.

"And now, you Mr. Tambo, s'pose you tell me when a door is not a door."

"What's that, Mr. Interlocutor? What did you say? When is a door not a door? Um—um. Let me see."

"Don't you know that, Mr. Tambo?"

"Just a minute. Let me disremember."

"Can't wait no longer, Mr. Tambo. A door's not a door when it's ajar."

After this everyone pounded the floor and cheered.

"They're making almost as much noise as they did at the big show," whispered Stevie.

"Sure, it's just as good a show," said Mit.

"Stevie'll make as good a minstrel as Daddy

122

Rice himself or maybe this new fellow called Christy," said one of the boys' fathers to Mr. Foster after the show.

Mr. Foster tried to be pleased, but it was hard. He didn't want any of his boys to be minstrels.

When the boys counted the money there was enough for them all to go to Daddy Rice's big show in Pittsburgh.

"Why don't we give a lot of shows this summer?" said Mit. "Then we could go to lots of shows." So from then on, the Minstrel Society gave regular shows.

Stevie could always be counted on to do something new and funny. Sometimes he made the audience feel like crying, too.

The Shanghai chicken, when you put him in the pit,

Visiting Around

FALL CAME. Stevie was growing up. For the first time he was really studying hard. Mr. Kelly and Pa were proud of his progress.

Once a week his long, thin legs carried him swiftly over the miles between Allegheny and Mr. Kleber's music shop in Pittsburgh. His lessons were free. Mr. Kleber said his most talented pupil must go on studying even if these were hard times for the Fosters.

Stevie was as happy and lively as a cricket. His frayed cuffs and patched pants didn't worry him in the least, but something else did.

Ann Elizabeth had married and taken her

banjo with her to her new home. Stevie's flageo-let was broken. The piano was sold. He had no instrument to play but Uncle Ned's tuner, and his music was far past that.

"Just you wait till next summer," he said one evening. "I'll save every penny I make from the minstrel shows and buy a banjo of my own."

"Good! Good!" said William with a grin.

"We'll make a business man of you yet," Pa said. "I've always heard that hard times were good for people."

"I'm going to be a business man, Pa," Stevie said promptly. "I'm going to write music and sell it and make money that way."

"That's not the kind of business I mean," Pa said. Mrs. Foster quickly changed the subject.

"William, you and young William are going to be away from home a great deal this winter," she said quietly. "Henry and Dunning are in business in Pittsburgh, and the girls are both married and in their own homes. I think Mit, Stevie, and I will visit them a while."

"But what about school?" asked Mit. "I'm at the head of my class."

"I wish I could take something along to make music with," Stevie said.

"I'll teach you, Mit," Ma said.

"I'll send you a Comic Songster, Stevie," Pa said with a twinkle in his eye.

Everyone laughed. A Comic Songster was a squeaky tin whistle which Daddy Rice used to make fun. No one could play a tune on it.

"Mit, you and Stevie go and bring in some wood," Pa said.

"They want to talk without us," Mit said.

"Maybe I could visit Uncle Struthers," Stevie said. "I've always wanted to. I'll miss school with Mr. Kelly, though. He says I'm doing real well, too."

"Maybe the Colbys would let me stay with

them and finish school," Mit said thoughtfully. "I could do things around their house and in school to pay my way."

Ma had her way, and a week later Stevie was visiting Etty instead of Uncle Struthers. Etty was a very strict teacher.

"I wish Pa would send that Comic Songster he promised me," Stevie said one day. "Maybe I could play some kind of tune on it."

"Write him a letter," said Etty. "That can be

your composition for the day. Write it carefully and don't misspell the words."

"Will you correct it so it will be perfect when Pa gets it?"

"Certainly not," Etty said firmly.

"I'd rather meet a bunch of mad bees than write to Pa," Stevie said. "He'll make me correct every word I miss ten times."

Stevie did his best, but even so the letter didn't look right to him.

                              Youngstown Jany 14th 1837

My dear father,

I wish you to send me a Comic Songster for you promised to. if I had my pensyl I could rule my paper or if I had the money to buy Black ink But if I had my whistle I would be so taken with it I donot think I would write atall. there has been a sleighing party this morning with twenty or thirty cupple Dr Bane got home last night and told us Henry was coming out here I wish Dunning would come with him and tell them both

to try to cone for I should like to see them both
most too much to talk about.

I remane your loving son
Stephen C. Foster

The letter came back promptly, but no Songster arrived. Stevie was told that it would be
sent when he made the corrections in his letter.
Stevie followed his father's directions, but when
the whistle came it only squeaked. He was disappointed and unhappy.

A short time later, however, Ma came to Etty's
for a two-week visit.

"After we leave here, Stevie, we'll spend the
summer with Uncle Struthers," she said. Stevie
danced a jig, but not before Etty.

Just dance out - side de door;

Hop to It,
Strangers

In July Stevie and his mother went to visit Uncle Struthers in Poland, Ohio. No one could have been happier than Stevie when they drove up to the big log cabin Uncle Struthers had built on a hill overlooking a river.

The old pioneer, who was eighty years old, met Stevie and his mother with a shout. An Indian carried in their boxes. A dog almost as big as a pony put its paws on Stevie's shoulders and washed his face for him. The supper table was set in the big room.

" 'Pears to me it's about time you-all paid me a visit," Uncle Struthers said heartily. "I heard

130

about you being at Etty's and Ann Eliza's. Just livin' 'round everywhere, but not here."

"But I'm gladder to be here than any place, Uncle Struthers," Stevie said. Ma nodded and smiled in agreement.

By the time he had been on the farm a month Stevie had learned to milk a cow. Uncle Struthers said that he had the "most natural milk hands." He meant that Stevie's long, slim fingers seemed to know exactly how to milk the most particular cow.

One morning Ma heard Stevie shouting. She looked outside and saw him running toward the cabin.

"Uncle Struthers! Uncle Struthers! They're coming. They're crossing the river. The Conestogas are crossing the river!"

Ma put down her knitting and stepped to the door. Stevie was racing across the yard waving his hat, his hair flying across his face.

131

"Ma, where's Uncle Struthers? I was down by the river. Folks in Conestoga wagons are getting ready to ford the river. They want to know if they can camp on this side and have some milk. Their cow died."

"Your uncle is down in the barnlot, dear," Ma said. "How many wagons are there?"

"Six, I think," Stevie shouted as he raced off toward the barn. Uncle Struthers heard him coming and chuckled as he saw him charging across the field.

"Like as not he's seen those Conestogas coming to the ford. Like as not he thinks they're about to cross. Don't suppose he knows how long it takes to get wagons ready to tow. He'll learn, though. Mighty smart boy, Stevie is," Uncle Struthers said out loud.

He talked to himself this way because he had spent so many years alone in the woods.

"Uncle Struthers! Uncle Struthers! There're

132

settlers getting ready to ford the stream at the sugar house. Come quick. They want to know, can they camp on our side and can they have some milk for the children? Their cow died," called Stevie.

He was out of breath when he reached his uncle. Uncle Struthers smiled at him and nodded. Then he turned and picked up a basket from the ground.

He leaned on the fence inside of which grunted a big sow and twelve little pigs.

"Uncle Struthers, did you hear what I said?"

"Now, Susy," said Uncle Struthers to the old sow, "that's as fine a family as I've seen you have for a long time. Don't hurry 'em. They grow better if you don't hurry 'em."

Stephen fidgeted. He started to speak again. This time Uncle Struthers walked away. Stephen followed him.

"There, now, Stevie," the old man said at last.

133

"What were you saying about some campers down by the river?"

Stephen told his story.

"So they want to camp on the bottom land? I don't know as I blame them. Maybe they would like a few nice apples and potatoes to take along too. We'll get them ready."

"But, Uncle Struthers, they want to know if they can camp. Can't I run tell them?"

Uncle Struthers shook his head. "Now, Stevie, they know they're welcome to camp," he said. "They won't make a fire for several hours. We'll be there by then."

"But, Uncle Struthers—I——"

"Come along. Bring two buckets from the shed. We'll pick some apples for them first."

Stephen lagged behind his uncle. He tried his best to see beyond the bluff. He wished now that he hadn't hurried so fast. He wished he could see the campers ford the stream.

134

But Uncle Struthers was walking straight ahead, going toward the apple orchard. There was nothing for Stephen to do but follow him.

"It's nigh a bumper crop this year," Uncle Struthers called back over his shoulder. "Pippins, red-cheeked, bakers, eaters, cookers, giveaways, and sellers. Every tree grew from seed planted by me and Johnny Appleseed."

"Who was Johnny Appleseed?" Stevie said.

"Don't rightly know," Uncle Struthers replied. "Some folks say his name was Chapman, but pioneers knew him—and loved him—as Johnny Appleseed." He stopped and looked into the distance.

"He's thinking about something a long way off," Stevie thought. "But I wish he wouldn't tell a story now. We'll be sure to miss the crossing."

"He was a little feller who wandered around, even in Indian land, planting apple seeds," Uncle Struthers added as he started up the hill.

135

"These trees was planted in the dark of the moon one night when Johnny come to tell me the Indians was on the warpath," the old man said. "There now, you climb up in that tree. We'll pick eaters first."

Stevie could hear shouts from beyond the bluff. He looked down at his uncle, who was examining each apple that Stevie shook down.

"Can't give traveling folks bad ones," Uncle Struthers explained. "Shake easy, son. Don't want to bruise 'em."

The two worked silently. The buckets were almost full when there was a loud shout from the direction of the stream.

"I guess they are clear across now," Stevie said crossly. "Why can't we do this tomorrow?"

"Don't get your dander up, Stevie, my lad," Uncle Struthers said, smiling. "Take off if you like. I'll foller along soon and we'll both see the crossing."

136

Stevie slid to the ground. "I'll do extra to-morrow," he said as he ran down the hill.

The path through the fields was worn by the cows going down to drink, but the grain on either side was almost as high as Stevie's head.

"Get over there, Jerry," came a shout.

"Mind that board. Don't let it crack. Lean back, Mom, the water ain't deep here," came another shout.

Stevie came panting out on the shore.

He couldn't believe his eyes. There, instead of the big lumbering wagon which he had expected to see crossing the stream, was a flat-bottom boat.

A man stood upright with a long pole in his hand. The boat was filled with furniture, and a woman and several children sat in the middle. A man on horseback splashed by its side. Four great brown oxen were swimming with their heads held high.

"Hello, there, Bud. We thought you had for-

gotten us," shouted the man on horseback. "Stand off them critters when they come ashore."

Stevie looked at the beasts whose eyes protruded with fright. Something like a chill ran up his back. He had never been nearer oxen than on the sidewalk in the city. But he'd show those men. There was a boy about his own age watching him from the boat. Stevie gulped and went to the spot where the first ox was headed.

"Step back, Stevie." It was Uncle Struthers' voice. "Give 'em time to paw a bit before you close in on 'em."

Stevie felt better. Uncle Struthers was there.

The first animal found its footing and lowered its head. Slowly it walked out of the water. For a second it looked about and then began to paw the wet earth.

"Slowly does it," said Uncle Struthers quietly.

Stevie walked directly toward the great beast. There was a rope about its neck. Stevie took hold of this. It was knotted about like a collar. Stevie untied it and the ox snorted and followed peacefully up the hill.

"Drat that second beast," shouted Uncle Struthers. "Drop downstream, Stevie. He's going ashore down there."

Stevie tethered the first ox and raced down the shore toward where the second was heading.

Other boats were putting out from the opposite shore. Some were farther up the stream and some were down the stream. Everyone was shouting. The whips of the men on horseback were cracking over the heads of the oxen as they were forced into the water.

"But Uncle Struthers," said Stevie. "Where do they carry the boats?"

"Ha! Ha! Ha!" came a strong voice from behind Stevie and Uncle Struthers. "Where do we carry the boats? You tell him, Jim."

Stevie whirled around. There were a man and

a boy of about his own size. They were both laughing. When they saw Stevie's face and how embarrassed he was they stopped.

"Sorry, lad," said the man. "Didn't mean to make fun. Jim here can tell you all about how we tote our 'boats.' Judge is my name, sir," he added, turning to Uncle Struthers.

"John Struthers," said Uncle. "Glad to see you. Come far?"

The two men walked off together. Stevie stood looking at the boy who had just been laughing at him.

"Say, let's get started," said Jim. "You goin' to help unload?"

That was all that Jim Judge said, but Stevie felt fine. He didn't mind being laughed at by people like these.

"Tell me about the boats," he said.

"Sure, but come on and help get the rest of these here ornery creatures."

For the next half hour the two boys worked hard herding the oxen as they came ashore.

When the last one was tethered to a tree, Jim sat down. Stevie followed.

"We don't have boats. Those are just the bottoms of wagons. We take off the wheels and calk up the sides and the wagons float. We don't have to do that when the stream ain't deep like this one. Most times we just drive across the river," he said.

"Stevie!" shouted Uncle Struthers. "Run tell your mother we'll be going t' have a lot o' folks for supper. Then you go down to the smoke house and fetch up a couple of hams."

All afternoon Steve and Jim wandered about the farm. Jim was excited over everything that he saw.

"We been on the way for the three months," he said. "I'll be awful glad when we get out to where we're going."

142

"Where are you going?"

"To some place beyond the big river, I guess. Pop's got an idea he wants a great big farm. It's getting pretty crowded back east."

All the women in the party came up to the log cabin. The children played about the yard and the men tinkered with the wagons and talked with Uncle Struthers.

Supper was exciting. There were so many people and everyone helped. After supper they all wandered back to where their wagons were standing in a circle.

"Seems right foolish about here to fix 'em that way," said Mr. Judge, "but it's the best protection against Indians out on the plains."

When it grew dark the pioneers built a great fire and then, for the first time, Stevie saw something which made his eyes shine. There were banjos and a fiddle and a flute belonging to people in the party.

Everyone, including Ma and Stevie and Uncle Struthers, sat about in a circle. Jim's brother began the music. It was a lively tune. All the young people jumped to their feet. Some of the older ones followed. Everybody danced. Those who didn't, clapped their hands. The banjos joined in. The children sang and whistled. The music got faster and faster.

"What's that tune?" said Stevie to his mother. "I don't know it."

"That's 'Pass Your Partner Round, Nelly,'" Jim said. "It's my favorite. Come on, dance. There's going to be a reel. My sister over there's a real good dancer. Her name's Jean."

Stevie first thought he wouldn't, but when everyone else took partners, he started around to where Jean sat. But she was already running toward him. She had two long braids of light brown hair and she was laughing as she grabbed Stevie's hand and pulled him into the circle.

144

On and on they all danced. The music changed. The dancers changed partners, but they never stopped. One by one the little children crawled near their mothers and went to sleep. The babies were carried back to the wagons to sleep. It was a very dark night, but with the fire and the stars it was beautiful.

When Stevie felt that he could hardly dance another step, the music suddenly stopped. It changed. The violin took the lead. It was softer. Everyone sat down and began to sing. The songs they sang were all hymns, beautiful hymns.

Then, after what seemed a very short time to Stevie, Jim's father took off his hat and everyone knelt down on the ground.

"The Lord is my shepherd," Jim's father began. Everyone joined in. "I shall not want."

Stevie and his mother knelt, too. They finished the Psalm and then Jim's father made a short prayer. After that the crowd scattered very

145

quickly. Almost by the time Stevie and his mother and Uncle Struthers had reached the house, everything was quiet.

"Makes me kind of lonesome," said Uncle Struthers. "Don't know as I might just join up with them, lad, and leave you and your ma to look after things here."

But Stevie knew that he was joking. Still, he knew too that it was just what Uncle Struthers would like to do better than anything else if he weren't eighty years old.

The crowd stayed for three days. When they left Stevie rode in the lead wagon with Jim for ten miles up the road to the next town.

As he walked he sang the tunes which he had learned the last three nights.

I dream of Jea-nie with the light brown hair,

Here, There, and Everywhere

THE SUMMER with Uncle Struthers was one of the nicest that Stevie could remember. He begged to stay on when his mother said they must live nearer where Pa was working.

"Let him stay on for a spell, Eliza," Uncle Struthers said quietly. "He has a feeling for the land. The animals take to him and so do I. He's old for his age. I need a feller like him."

"He is still a child, John. I must have him with me. He and Mit must go to school. I must see that he has on his proper flannels when winter comes," Ma said.

"But, Ma, I don't like school," Stevie said.

"Please, Ma, let me stay." But Ma merely looked at him and shook her head.

Stevie ran off for another look at his own fat hog, a rubdown for the big farm horse, and a quick walk by the river. He wished Ma didn't think of him as a little boy. He was going on twelve now and thought he was grown up.

So Stevie had to leave the cows and pigs, the apple orchard, the fields, the pumpkins, and the corn, the coon hunting and the long days of fishing and dreaming with Uncle Struthers. He and his mother and Mit moved into a nice boarding house in town.

This was only the first of many such moves. During the next three years Ma, Mit, and Stevie moved many times.

Then one day, when they were living in Piqua, Ohio, Mit came bursting into the sitting room where Stevie was reading and Ma was sewing.

"It's come! The letter's come!" he shouted,

waving a letter before her eyes. "I have a job as first clerk and messenger with McCormack and Brackenridge in Pittsburgh. It's for two years or longer if I do well."

"That's great!" Stevie shouted. "When do you go? You can take my gray coat. I can wear Pa's old one."

"Wait till you hear what I get," Mit went on. "One hundred dollars a year, my board and food, washing, and a small horse to ride. I don't have to clean any lamps or the warehouse after work or do anything that will get my clothes dirty, and I'm to be called *Mr. Foster* even by the wharf hands."

"I'm proud of you, Morrison," Ma said with a happy smile. "Very proud. When do you go?"

"Tomorrow. Look, they even sent me this money to pay my way. I'll go by stagecoach, canal boat, and train. I wish you could go, too, Stevie," he added.

"I wish I could, too," Stevie said. "Ma, maybe I could get a job helping Mr. Kleber and live with Mit."

"You're only fourteen, Stevie," Ma said. "You must stay here and go to school."

Stevie frowned.

When Mr. Foster came home that week he was proud of Mit but worried about Stevie's poor showing in school. He didn't know the nights Stevie spent reading history and fine poetry by candlelight. He didn't know that Stevie was already writing verses for his tunes.

One day early in January, 1840, William came for a visit. Everyone but Stevie seemed to know that he was coming. Etty and her husband and Ann Eliza and hers were there, too.

Then, before Stevie had anything to say about it, the family decided that he was to go with William on a three-hundred-mile trip to Athens Academy near Towanda, Pennsylvania.

150

"But why must I go to school?" Stevie asked with a frown. "I don't like school except for Mr. Kelly's. Please, Pa, don't make me go."

But the family shook their heads, and before he knew it the morning came for Stevie and William to leave.

It was snowing, and there were great drifts of snow piled along the roads.

151

"We'll write often," Ma said. "Be a good boy and study hard and, Stevie, be sure and wear your flannels under your shirt."

"Oh, Ma, Stephen's not a baby. He's fourteen," William said. "Come on, passenger."

Stevie swallowed hard. He was glad that William had said this, but he hated to have Ma look so tearful. He gave her a hug and hopped into the sleigh.

The snow under the runners of the sleigh was icy. The horses pranced. The bells rang, and William and Stephen sang. It was wonderful.

At noon they had dinner in the home of a friend of William's. William introduced Stevie as "my brother, Stephen, who is on his way to Athens Academy in Pennsylvania."

For the first time in his life adults treated him as one of themselves. Stevie sat very straight in his high-backed chair. At one time a point of history came up in the conversation and Stevie knew the answer. After dinner everyone went to the sitting room, where Stevie saw a beautiful piano standing near the window. He stopped to look at it.

"Do you play, Stephen?" his hostess asked.

"Yes, Ma'am. Do you know a new song called 'Comin' Through the Rye'? The words are by the poet Robert Burns. May I play it for you?"

William was amazed to learn how well Stephen played. He was also amazed by Stephen's fine manners, but most of all he was amazed to see how little shyness Stephen showed among strangers. William was proud of his brother.

That night the two of them stayed at a hotel. Here the talk about the fire was all of politics. Stephen had nothing to say but listened well. "Maybe the boy really does belong in the music world," William thought. "It's the one place where he seems at home."

All the way from Youngstown he and Stephen

stayed in the homes of friends or in good hotels. It was an exciting trip for both of them.

When they reached Pittsburgh, Mit and Dunning were waiting for them. The four had not been together for some time.

"William, we have tickets to Christy's Minstrels for tonight and tomorrow night," Mit said. "But right now we've got to take Stevie someplace. Will you come with us?"

William thanked him but said that he had some business to look after.

"Come on, Stevie," Mit went on. "We have a surprise for you." He and Stevie and Dunning hurried along the street. "We're giving you a present, Stevie, but we're going to let you do your own picking."

They passed several new stores and turned into Henry Kleber's music shop. The old musician hugged Stevie and kissed him on both cheeks as Germans often did in those days.

Mr. Kleber called into the back room and several of his friends came out. Mit and Dunning were amazed and impressed by the warmth with which they greeted Stevie.

"We've come to buy a clarinet for Stevie," Dunning said. "We want him to pick it out."

Mr. Kleber played each of the five clarinets he had for sale. Stevie listened carefully. When he made his choice Mr. Kleber smiled and nodded. He winked at Dunning and Mit.

"He chose the best one. He has the true ear, that boy. Now, Stevie, watch me. So. Moisten your lips. Fingers like this. Blow gently."

Stevie tried.

The noises that came from the clarinet made everyone laugh. Stevie tried again and again.

Mit and Dunning went to pay the bill. They shook their heads and talked a bit, but Stevie thought little of it until they were walking away from the shop. Then he stopped suddenly.

"Was it too expensive, Dunning? I never thought of that. I could take it——"

"Just take care of it, Stevie," Mit said. "It *was* more than we expected."

"You'll have to begin thinking about such things, but not now," Dunning said with a smile. "We want you to have the clarinet you want."

That evening and the next, the four Foster brothers sat in the front row of the theater watching the great minstrel Christy. They shouted and clapped and stamped with the rest of the audience.

The second evening Dunning, who was a friend of Christy, took Stevie and Mit backstage. Dunning told Christy about the minstrel shows Stevie and Mit and their friends had put on. Christy clapped them on the back.

"Like to think of young minstrels coming along," he said. "It's the best entertainment in the country."

"Mr. Christy, if I write a really good song, would you play it?" Stevie asked suddenly.

"What's that? You're going to write songs? Sure, I'll try them out. But make them lively so folks can laugh." Christy grinned and turned away. "Have to go now."

"For goodness' sake, Stevie, why did you say that?" Dunning asked as the boys left.

"I wanted to know," Stevie said. "You know, that's what I'm going to do when I finish school."

"Why, Christy's the best minstrel in the country, even better than Daddy Rice," Mit said.

"I know it, but my songs will be good, too."

William smiled, but he wondered if he was doing the right thing in taking Stevie to Athens Academy. "But of course I am," he thought. "The boy's only a child still. He'll forget all this when he's out of college." But even so William wasn't so sure.

Before it seemed possible, the visit in Pittsburgh was over and Stevie and William were on their way to the Academy.

It was evening when they arrived. When they came into the square around which the inns and the church were built, they came to a stop behind several Conestoga wagons.

Stevie watched them and wondered what had happened to Jim Judge.

"There's the school, Stephen," said William, pointing. "That building over there with the high white pillars. See, the one into which all those boys are going."

Stevie looked. It was a beautiful building, and the boys looked as if they would be fun, but Stevie had never got along very well with a large group of boys.

"Do I have to live with all those boys?" he asked. "Couldn't I live with you, William, and come over to school?"

"No, but I've arranged for you to live right

over there in that white house with Mr. Herrick and his family. I thought you'd like that."

As the fine sleigh jingled by the school, Stevie saw that the boys were all throwing snowballs. Several waved to him. Stevie smiled. Maybe it wasn't going to be so bad.

The sleigh stopped before Mr. Herrick's. Stevie saw that there were several small children looking out of the window. A short fat man opened the door. A tall thin woman stood in the background. She led the way up to Stevie's room.

"The young gentleman should be very comfortable here, sir," said Mrs. Herrick. "It's a nice room with a fireplace and I'll be glad to treat him just like one of my own family."

Stevie looked about him. It was very cold in the room now. The curtains were dark and the carpet was worn. There was a small wooden table with a straight chair before it. A lamp stood on the table.

160

"The view from this window is the very nicest in the house," said Mrs. Herrick. "It looks right down over the river."

This was the best thing Stevie had heard yet.

"See that he has plenty of wood," said brother William. "I will pay you extra for that."

Then William left. Stevie was alone. He went to the window to look out but it was too dark to see the river. It was too cold to stay up and no one brought him wood for the fire. Stevie went to bed.

He pulled on his coat over his night clothes and took his new clarinet from its box.

"It won't matter if I play it real soft tonight," he said to himself happily. "I have no lessons to get."

For the first few days at Athens Academy Stephen was homesick, cold, and hungry. He was homesick because he knew no one. He was cold because Mr. Herrick brought him no wood and

and at first he didn't ask for it. He was hungry because there was little food for him.

But one afternoon, after a big snow, he was walking across the yard between the school and his boarding house with his books under his arm. He came upon a big boy washing a little boy's face with snow. Stephen's temper flared.

He pulled the little boy aside and faced the big one alone.

"You do that again and I'll wash your face in snow and grind it in as sure as my name's Stephen Collins Foster," he said.

"And we'll help," said a boy about his own size, who had come up with several others. The big boy left without further trouble and Stephen started on.

"Say, Foster, aren't you the 'tooter' from over at old Herrick's?" asked the boy. "I'm James Forbes and this is William Warner. Come study in the library with us. It's warm there."

The little boy had disappeared. Stephen, James, and William hurried into a big paneled room heated by a round stove.

"We can't talk here. Pull up a chair," James whispered. Stephen settled himself. Several boys grinned at him and he felt more at home.

That evening he asked for wood. He would study in the library, but he wanted to read at night in his room.

"You don't need wood of evenings," Mr. Herrick said. "You ought to be in bed and asleep. What's more, if you're going to drink two glasses of milk you can pay for the extra one."

"And you can stop all that caterwauling in your room," Mrs. Herrick said. "It keeps the children awake."

That evening Stephen wrote William a long letter. "It's a nice school," he wrote. "I'm doing good work, especially in Latin and History. I have two friends, James Forbes and William

Warner, but I'd rather be with you in Towanda. Couldn't I come there and live with you and go to school there?"

He ended the letter by saying, "Don't pay Mr. Herrick for a fire in my room as I haven't had any wood since I came."

William answered the letter, but not before something had happened that changed Stephen's ideas about Athens Academy very much.

And the wood - land birds are sing-ing

The Tioga Waltz

"WHAT ARE you doing on Free Day tomorrow?"
James asked Stevie as they left Latin class together one day. "William and I are going to call
on Miss Frances Welles and have some music
and tea. She suggested that we bring you along."

"What do you mean, going to have music?"
Stevie asked.

"Miss Welles plays the piano and we take our
flutes along and have fun together. You're to
bring your clarinet."

"When do we go?" Stevie was so excited he
could think of nothing else.

"Twelve o'clock. We'll stop for you, Foster."

The next day was clear and bright. Each of the boys carried his instrument under his arm. First they went down into a valley and then through a woods. It was a long walk, but Stevie enjoyed every foot of it.

"This is an old Indian trail," James told him as they followed a ridge. "Down there is the Chemung River. On that bluff over there there used to be an Indian village called Te-a-o-ga, the Meeting Place."

"That stone house is where we're going," William added. "All that high ground is called Tioga Point and belongs to the Welles family."

Miss Frances met the boys at the door. She was a pretty young woman who greeted Stevie with a smile that he never forgot.

"I hear you're quite a 'tooter,' Mr. Foster," she said. "A clarinet will add a great deal to our pleasure."

Mrs. Welles greeted them from her chair be-

166

side the fireplace in the big living room. The light of the flames flickered on the shining wood of the large piano.

Stevie was sure there never had been such an afternoon. Miss Frances had books of songs printed in parts. Stevie read music poorly, but after the others played a song he could follow it easily. This was his first experience with this kind of fun.

"Did you ever try to write a song of your own?" Miss Frances asked him as they cracked nuts and ate gingerbread before the fire.

"That's what I'm going to do," Stevie said quietly. "I don't know much about it yet."

"Perhaps I can help you," said Miss Frances. "I've studied with a good teacher, but I can't dream up tunes."

"Would you really?" Stevie cried.

"Here, here!" James said. "Miss Frances is *our* friend. You can't take over."

"Oh, I—I—didn't mean——" Stevie was embarrassed. The boys laughed.

"Don't be so serious, Foster. We're glad you came along. Didn't you say you could play a banjo? Miss Frances has one."

Stevie tuned the banjo up and began to play.

Soon the colored servants were peeking in through the door. The boys took turns prancing about the room with Miss Frances, and Mrs. Welles clapped.

"Look outside," James said suddenly. "Almost dark. It'll be two weeks anyhow before we get another Free Day, but this was worth it."

All three boys were reprimanded at school for being late, but Stevie didn't care. He had found three new friends and knew he would soon know how to put down on paper those little black notes which brought music to everyone.

Stevie took only a few lessons from Miss Frances when she and her mother decided to take a trip to Europe. They would not be back for a long time. Meanwhile James and William were busy studying for final exams before graduating in June, and did not have time for Stevie.

He was alone and homesick, and his shyness increased. Finally he wrote another letter begging William to let him go to school in Towanda so they could be together.

April came, the hardest month of the year to stay inside. Stevie fell behind in his schoolwork and Mr. Marvin, the headmaster, said he was lazy. He began to play hookey.

One day Stevie was down by the Chemung River when James and William came hunting him. They had news for him, they said.

"Mr. Marvin wants some extra music for our commencement," James began, "something kind of different——"

"And I said your music would be better than any old bought piece," William added.

"You know I don't know how to write music," Stevie said. "I just play what I hear in my head." But his eyes shone and his cheeks were red. "What kind of music does he want?" he went on. "A march, a love song, a jig, a——" He jumped to his feet. "A waltz! You know, like this—hum, hum, hum, oh, hummy, hum, hum. I know! I have one in my head." He started up the path.

"Stevie, wait!" James called. "Mr. Marvin said your work had to come up or——" But Stevie was gone.

The boys grinned at each other.

"He'll do it, and it'll be great," James said as they walked back to school.

Stevie spent every minute he could on the music. His school work came up, too.

"I'll play the first part and you can play the second and third parts," he said. "I'll write it for four flutes and then if we can't get anyone else we'll just have three parts."

170

The great day came. Brother William was coming over from Towanda. Stevie had a new suit and his face shone. He called his new piece "The Tioga Waltz" in honor of Miss Frances.

There was a big crowd at the commencement. There were several songs and a talk. Then the three boys with two flutes and a clarinet stepped forward on the stage.

Stevie announced the piece. He didn't mind doing this at all. It made him think of the minstrel shows that he had performed in at home. Everyone clapped. The music began.

It was a quiet little piece, but the crowd liked it. They clapped and clapped even before Mr. Marvin stepped out on the platform. The boys had hurried back of the curtain.

"Ladies and gentlemen," he began. "The composition you have just heard was composed and arranged by one of our very talented pupils, Stephen Collins Foster. Stephen played the clar-

inet. Stephen, will you please step out on the platform again."

This time Stevie's knees were shaking. James and William pushed him forward. He bowed. The audience clapped, and he bowed again. He hoped William had come. This would make him proud.

He held the music of his "Tioga Waltz" in his cold hand. It was his first contribution to the profession he wanted so much to follow.

After the graduation William and Stevie sat on the bank of the Chemung River, talking.

"Stephen," William said, "I was proud of you today. Everyone who came up to me, including Mr. Marvin, spoke of your talent."

Stevie beamed. "Then may I go home and get started writing songs, William? I'll be lonely here when William and James leave."

"Mr. Marvin tells me you could make a fine record if you tried. Doesn't that interest you?"

"There's only one thing I want to do."

"But you're not fifteen. You're sure to change your mind, and then it may be too late to go to college. I can't always support you."

"I'll not change my mind. I wanted to make up songs when I was four. Ask Ma. I told her."

The two brothers faced each other, the one a strong, successful, and determined businessman, the other almost a failure in school but equally determined. Stephen was the first to smile.

"Please, William. I'll work hard. I'll help Ma and Pa. I'll go to school in Allegheny if you wish and—I'll make a go of writing music."

"At least you may go home for the summer," William said with a smile. "Collect your things. I'll pay the bills and see Mr. Marvin."

Tioga Waltz

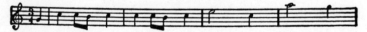

"I'll Make a Go of It"

THE FOSTERS were living in a new home in Allegheny which William had built for them. Mr. and Mrs. Foster, Mit, and Dunning greeted the travelers. There were tears of happiness in Ma's eyes when Stevie gave her a big hug.

"Stevie, it's good to have you home. Let me look at you. How did the graduation music come out? You must play it right away."

"His waltz was a great success, Ma," William said. "I was very proud of him. More than one person told me how hard it is to write music in parts."

"Miss Frances showed me a little about it be-

175

fore she went away," Stevie said. "It was fun, really, to try to get the three instruments to sound well together."

They went on into the hall. Doors opened from the hall into the sitting room and the parlor. Stevie glanced into the parlor.

"You have a piano again!" he shouted. "I wondered if you would." He hurried into the parlor, sat down at the piano, and began to play "The Tioga Waltz."

"May I have the honor of this dance, Ma'am?" Dunning said to his mother. Pa and Mit clapped as the two danced around the room to Stevie's music. Oh, this was fun!

Supper was fun, too, and afterward the family sat on the steps of the back porch, talking. Finally Stevie and William began to yawn.

"It was a long trip," William said. "Come on, Stevie. We'll let the others talk about us."

"Just a minute," Pa said. "I want to tell Stevie what plans we have for him. I've arranged for him to study mathematics this summer with my friend Mr. Moody. Then we'll try to get him an appointment to the Naval Academy."

Stevie heard Dunning whisper, "That will make him forget about his music," and he jumped to his feet.

"Pa, I'm grown up now. I want to compose music and that's what I'm going to do. I'll never forget music, Dunning. It's part of me. Can't you see that? Can't any of you understand that?"

The others looked at him in amazement.

"Of course, Stevie, of course," Pa said. "Don't get so excited."

"I'm not, but I don't like school and I do like music, and I want to make up my own mind!"

For a moment no one spoke. Then Dunning cleared his throat. "I believe you mean it, Stevie. But why not study with old Moody? You never know when you might need to know figures."

"We'll make decisions in the fall," Ma said. She took Stevie's arm with one hand and William's with the other, and the three went inside.

The next day Stevie walked into Pittsburgh to visit his old friends at the music shop. They made him feel welcome and happy.

"So you wrote a song," Mr. Kleber said. "Let's hear it." He handed Stevie a clarinet.

Stevie expected his friends to be enthusiastic, but they weren't. Mr. Kleber shook his head.

"Not a bad tune, but you can do better, Stephen," he said. "Wait on customers once a week for me and I'll teach you the little I know about composition."

Stevie nodded, but he was dreadfully disappointed. His friends who really knew music did not like "The Tioga Waltz."

He touched the keys of a beautiful square piano. "I want a piano like this for my own," he said. "I just *have* to sell songs."

179

"Then you'd better have another string to your bow," Mr. Kleber said.

"What do you mean?" asked Stevie.

"He means you'd better find some way to make a living besides writing music," said the violinist. "You should go back to school."

"Mr. Koontz is right," Mr. Kleber said quietly. "You may change your mind about music."

"Why does everybody say that? I'm going to start writing songs tomorrow," Stevie said.

"Good! But if you knew figures I could give you a job now," said Mr. Kleber. "I can't use a poor piano player. Think about it, Stevie."

Stevie did. What his musical friends said mattered to him. It hurt that Mr. Kleber called him a poor musician. "I'll show him," Stevie thought. "But maybe he's right about the figures."

Pa and Ma were surprised when he agreed to study mathematics, but they were pleased, too.

Now Stephen really worked, both on his mathematics and on his music. Pa thought he "fid-diddled" on the piano too much, but Ma knew he was composing music for a poem she liked.

Stevie failed in his examinations for the Naval Academy the following year, but he didn't care. One afternoon he came home beaming.

"Did you find a gold brick?" asked Ma.

"No, but I mailed my music to a publisher in Philadelphia today," he said. "No one knows it but you and Mr. Kleber."

Weeks passed and he received no answer. Then one evening in December, 1844, when he was almost eighteen, Stevie had a surprise.

He came home later than usual, but a low light was burning in the room the way Ma always left it. Stephen started to put it out.

"Surprise! Surprise!" someone shouted.

"Surprise, Stephen!" many voices called. Other lamps were lighted and Stephen saw his friends.

"It's come, Stephen," said Henry Kleber. "The

song you wrote is here. You are a publishing musician now."

Someone put a copy of Stephen's first printed song on the piano.

"Play it for us, Stevie," Ma said. "Play 'Open Thy Lattice, Love.'"

Stephen began to smile. It was there before him, his own music. He took it in his hands. He read the title page over slowly to himself.

"Come, Stephen," said Mr. Kleber. "We're waiting to sing." Stephen began to play.

He wasn't looking at his music. Instead he was seeing stacks of music, each piece with his name on it. He was thinking of all the melodies he had heard as a boy. He knew that he had hundreds more in his heart.

"I made a go of it," he thought happily.

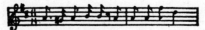

O - pen thy lattice, love, Listen to me!

Music
Everywhere

AFTER HIS first song was published Stephen still dreamed, but he was putting his dreams into action. He made more and more friends and went to gay parties. He joined a club called "The Knights of the S. T."

This was a secret club made up of young men who enjoyed one another's company. They held frequent meetings at which they talked and sang Stephen's songs as they came out. They could be counted on to help people in need.

In the fall of 1846 the Mexican War began. All the Knights enlisted, but Stephen was turned down. He felt unhappy.

Then Dunning enlisted and needed a reliable bookkeeper to take his place in the business in Cincinnati. Stephen offered to take the job.

Once more he leaned over the rail of a riverboat on the Ohio River. He watched the water foaming over the wheel and listened to the Negroes singing as they worked.

At one landing he saw a group of Conestoga wagons going West. He remembered those other pioneers who had danced to the music of banjos and violins at Uncle Struthers' farm.

He pulled a half-written song from his bag. He hummed the melody and corrected a few words. He finished the song the first week he was in Cincinnati and called it "Oh! Susanna."

That winter the great Christy and his minstrel show came to town. Stephen went backstage to see him. The minstrel laughed when Stephen reminded him that he had promised to write a song for him.

"Here it is," Stephen said. "It's good. Try it." Christy did and played it that very night before a large audience. By the next day it was being sung all over the city.

It wasn't fair of Christy to use the song. It had never been copyrighted and when Stephen tried to sell it he received only $100, even though the publisher made thousands from it.

But Stephen didn't care. Wherever he went about the city he heard people singing and playing "Oh! Susanna." It became a folk song overnight. The Forty-niners sang it on their way to California, and no minstrel show was popular unless it played the song.

In 1850 Dunning returned to the office and Stephen went to Baltimore and New York to see music publishers. He signed contracts with two firms that gave him two cents for each copy of his music sold.

Now that he was prosperous, Stephen went

home to ask Jane McDowell to marry him. The wedding took place on July 22, 1850.

During the next five years Stephen Foster wrote some of his finest songs. There were "Old Folks at Home," "Massa's in de Cold Ground," "My Old Kentucky Home," "Old Dog Tray," and "Jeannie with the Light Brown Hair."

Then his contracts ran out and he had to sign new ones. But he was tired now and his songs were not so good as his earlier ones. He went to New York to get new ideas and to try to pull things together. While there he fell ill and died on January 13, 1864.

The country soon forgot his poor songs and sang only the good ones. It remembered him as a great writer of simple melodies that have brought joy and peace and laughter to the world.

Old mul ley cow come onto de track,

Many Years
Afterward

It was a beautiful Fourth of July in the year 1951. A group of Boy Scouts was gathered about their scoutmaster, Mr. Harris. They stood at the edge of the New York University campus in a section of New York City known as the Bronx. They were waiting to tour the Hall of Fame.

Mr. Harris pointed to a large domed building that stood in the center of the campus. "That's the Gould Memorial Library," he said. "The colonnade surrounding it is the Hall of Fame for Famous Americans."

"What's the Hall of Fame?" asked a boy.

"It's a building erected to house one hundred

and fifty bronze busts and tablets commemorating famous Americans," Mr. Harris answered.

"Stephen Foster was the first musician to be put in the Hall of Fame," said a boy from Pittsburgh. "I know because the Stephen Foster Memorial Hall at the University of Pittsburgh has the best collection of things about Foster."

"Most of that collection was made by a friend of my grandfather," said a boy from Indiana. "His name was Josiah K. Lilly and he lived in Indianapolis, where I do."

"There are fine memorials to Foster in almost every state in the Union," said Mr. Harris.

"I'll bet we have the best one," said a boy from Georgia. "The Suwannee River Foster wrote about rises in the Okefenokee Swamp in Georgia. There's a monument to him in Fargo, too."

" 'Way Down Upon the Swanee River' is our State song," said a tall boy from Florida. "Foster spelled the name of the river wrong."

189

"Our memorial is a granite stone taken from land near where Foster wrote 'The Tioga Waltz,'" said a boy from Athens, Pennsylvania.

"Now, boys, let's be dignified and quiet while we go through the Hall of Fame," said Mr. Harris. He led the boys through the porchlike colonnade that almost encircled the library.

The boys looked with interest at the busts of authors, scientists, artists, educators, businessmen, inventors, and others they passed. Finally one boy said, "Here's Foster's bust. It's just his head and shoulders."

"Yes, his bust is where it ought to be," said Mr. Harris. "It's here with all the other men who had a dream and followed it."

Beauti-ful dream - er, wake un-to me,....

190

Old Folks at Home

S. C. F.

Stephen C. Foster

Way down up-on de Swa-nee Riv-er, Far, far a-
All up and down de whole cre-a-tion, Sad-ly I
All roun' de lit-tle farm I wan-dered, When I was
When I was play-ing with my broth-er, Hap-py was

way, Dere's wha' my heart is turning ev-er, Dere's wha' de
roam, Still long-ing for de old plan-ta-tion, And for de
young, Den man-y hap-py days I squan-dered, Man-y de
I, Oh, take me to my kind old moth-er, There let me

old folks stay.
old folks at home. } All de world am sad and drear-y,
songs I sung.
live and die.

Ev-'ry-where I roam; Oh! Dark-ies, how my

heart grows wear-y, Far from de old folks at home.

Oh! Susanna

S. C. F.

Stephen C. Foster

I came to Al-a-bam-a wid my ban-jo on my knee, I'm
rained all night de day I left, de weather it was dry, De

gwine to Lou'-si-an-a, my __ true love for to see. It
sun so hot I froze to death, Su-san-na, don't you

cry. Oh! Su-san-na, oh, don't you cry for me, For I'm

gwine to Lou'-si-an-a wid my ban-jo on my knee.

More About This Book

WHEN STEPHEN FOSTER LIVED

1826   STEPHEN COLLINS FOSTER WAS BORN NEAR PITTSBURGH, PENNSYLVANIA, JULY 4.

There were twenty-four states in the Union.

John Quincy Adams was President.

The population of the country was about 11,570,000.

1826
1841   STEVIE GREW UP NEAR PITTSBURGH, PENNSYLVANIA.

Peter Cooper built the first steam locomotive in the United States, 1830.

Cyrus McCormick invented the reaper, 1831.

Samuel Morse invented the telegraph, 1835.

American settlers reached Oregon, 1836.

Martin Van Buren was President, 1837-1841.

1841–
1844   STEVIE ATTENDED SCHOOL, STUDIED WITH TUTORS, AND COMPOSED "THE TIOGA WALTZ."

William Henry Harrison became President and died, 1841.

John Tyler was President, 1841-1845.

1844–1848   FOSTER HAD HIS FIRST SONGS PUBLISHED.

James K. Polk was President, 1845-1849.

Texas was annexed by the United States, 1845.

Elias Howe invented the sewing machine, 1846.

1848–1860   FOSTER COMPOSED "OH! SUSANNA," "MY OLD KENTUCKY HOME," AND OTHER POPULAR SONGS.

Zachary Taylor was President, 1849-1850.

California became a state, 1850.

Harriet Beecher Stowe's *Uncle Tom's Cabin* was published, 1852.

1860–1864   FOSTER LIVED IN NEW YORK CITY, A POOR AND UNHAPPY INDIVIDUAL.

Eleven states seceded from the Union and formed the Confederate States of America, 1860-1861.

The War between the States was fought, 1861-1865.

The Emancipation Proclamation was issued, 1863.

Lincoln delivered a famous address at Gettysburg, 1863.

194

1864   STEPHEN FOSTER DIED IN NEW YORK CITY, JANUARY 13.

There were twenty-four states in the Union and eleven in the Confederacy.

Abraham Lincoln was President of the Union and Jefferson Davis of the Confederacy.

The population was about 34,390,000.

DO YOU REMEMBER?

1. How did Stevie and his three older brothers celebrate Stevie's fourth birthday?

2. What new song about the flag did Stephen learn on his birthday?

3. What story did Mr. Foster tell the members of his family?

4. What happened when Stevie started to Dame Harvey's school?

5. How did Stevie get to hear a man play a banjo in Pittsburgh?

6. How did Stevie manage to get a new flageolet in Pittsburgh?

7. What long trip did Mrs. Foster, Henrietta, and Stevie take down the Ohio River?

8. Why was Stevie so happy with school when Mr. Kelly was his teacher?

9. What kind of show did Mit, Stevie, and others put on in the carriage house?

10. What interesting experiences did Stevie have with pioneers crossing Uncle Struthers' farm?

11. Why did Stevie write "The Tioga Waltz"?

12. How did Stevie's friends help him celebrate having his first song published?

13. How was Foster's famous song, "Oh Susanna," first played and published?

14. What are Foster's most famous songs?

IT'S FUN TO LOOK UP THESE THINGS

1. What were Conestoga wagons?

2. Why did pioneers often use oxen rather than horses to pull their wagons?

3. What is a minstrel song, and how does it differ from other kinds of music?

4. What does it mean to play a musical instrument by ear?

5. What other famous musicians besides Stephen Foster can you name?

6. What is the Hall of Fame where many great men, including Foster, are honored?

INTERESTING THINGS YOU CAN DO

1. Locate Pittsburgh and tell why many pioneer families passed through the city on their way West.

2. Draw a map to show how the Allegheny and Monongahela Rivers form the Ohio River.

3. Make a list of the most popular songs that Foster composed.

4. Join with others in the class in singing one of Foster's songs.

6. Display pictures of different musical instruments mentioned in the book.

5. Find out what different musical instruments Foster played during his lifetime.

OTHER BOOKS YOU MAY ENJOY READING

Book about Music Makers, Bruno Frost. Maxton.

Francis Scott Key: Maryland Boy, Augusta Stevenson. Trade and School Editions, Bobbs-Merrill.

How Music Grew, Marion Bauer and Ethel Peyser. Putnam.

John Philip Sousa: Marching Boy, Ann Weil. Trade and School Editions, Bobbs-Merrill.

Stephen Foster: His Life, Catherine Owens Peare. Holt.

Stephen Foster Songs, arranged for piano by Lev and Commins. Random House.

Story of Stephen Foster, Esther Douty. Grosset.

INTERESTING WORDS IN THIS BOOK

academy (ă kăd'ĕ mĭ) : private school

arranged (ă rānjd') : put in order

aweigh (ă wā') : clear of the ground, as an anchor, so that a ship can move

barge (bärj) : small flat-bottomed boat used on rivers and canals

bluff (blŭf) : steep, high bank

colonnade (kŏl'ŏ nād') : row or rows of columns set equal distances apart

commencement (kŏ mĕns'mĕnt) : ceremony at which persons are graduated

commemorating (kǒ měm'ổ rāt'ĭng) : honoring the memory of a person or event

commissioner (kǒ mĭsh'ŭn ẚr) : person possessing some sort of authority either individually or as a member of a group

Conestoga wagon (kǒn'ĕs tō'gȧ wăg'ŭn) : broad-wheeled covered wagon which pioneers used in traveling West

contribution (kǒn'trĭ bū'shŭn) : offering, gift

decision (dĕ sĭzh'ŭn) : conclusion, usually as a basis for action

deputy (dĕp'ừ tĭ) : subordinate officer, person chosen to represent another

exceptionally (ĕk sĕp'shŭn ăl ĭ) : in an unusual or uncommon manner

fidgeted (fĭj'ĕt ĕd) : moved restlessly

flageolet (flăj'ổ lĕt') : small wood-wind instrument somewhat like a flute

flannels (flăn'ĕlz) : underclothes made of soft woolen material

frayed (frād) : worn

interlocutor (ĭn'tẽr lŏk'ừ tẽr) : man who questions the comedians in a minstrel show

199

jimson (jĭm's'n) : tall weed with large white flowers

lumbering (lŭm'bēr ĭng) : moving clumsily

minstrel (mĭn'strĕl) : member of a theatrical group who dresses as a Negro and sings Negro songs

pioneer (pī'ȯ nēr') : early settler

primly (prĭm'lĭ) : stiffly, precisely

prosperous (prŏs'pēr ŭs) : successful

prow (prou) : front end of a boat

reliable (rė lī'à b'l) : dependable

reprimanded (rĕp'rĭ mănd'ĕd) : criticized severely, called to task

sentinel (sĕn'tĭ nĕl) : guard

snood (snōōd) : ribbon worn around the hair

tambourine (tăm'bōō rēn') : small drum with loose metal disks around the sides, played by shaking or hitting with the knuckles

tethered (tĕth'ērd) : tied

tinkered (tĭngk'ērd) : pottered, worked to repair something

tuckered (tŭk'ērd) : tired out

wharf (hwôrf) : platform beside a river or harbor where ships are loaded or unloaded

200